DINOSAUR QUEST

John Sibbick • Steve Parker

The dramatic history of the dinosaur hunters

Bounty
Books

This edition published in 2005 by Bounty Books
a division of Octopus Publishing Group Ltd
2-4 Heron Quays, London E14 4JP

ISBN 0 7537 1243 1
ISBN 13 9780753712436

Designed by Jane Hawkins
Produced by Bailey Publishing Associates for
Cornwall Editions Ltd,
8 Langurtho Road,
Fowey,
Cornwall PL23 1EQ,
UK

Printed and bound in the UK

1 3 5 7 9 10 8 6 4 2

Picture Acknowledgements (t=top, b=bottom, l=left, r=right)
4, 5t, 7b, 13b, 27, 29t, 31b, 32, 44, 45r, 52, 68, 80l, 85l ©
The Natural History Museum, London; 7t, 33b, 86, 87b
De Agostini/NHMPL; 25 © David Bayliss/RIDA/ GeoScience
Features PL; 26l, 29b © Mary Evans PL; 30 © A. Gragera,
Latin Stock/SPL; 31t, 33t © Geological Society/NHMPL;
36 © University of Pennsylvania; 37t, 51t Courtesy of the
Library, American Museum of Natural History; 37b ©
The Academy of Natural Sciences of Philadelphia, Ewell Sale
Stewart Library; 38 © Museum of Natural Sciences, Brussels,
Belgium; 41 © Jim Amos/SPL; 43 © Bettmann/Corbis; 45l ©
Museum für Naturkunde Humboldt-Universität zu Berlin; 46 ©
SPL; 48 © John Sibbick/National Geographic Image Collection;
53t Dr Martin Williams; 54 Courtesy of Alain Thomas
Photography Atopviews.com; 55b © Topfoto.co.uk; 56t,b ©
psihoyos.com; 57 © John Sibbick/National Geographic Image
Collection; 58, 75b, 91 © David Varricchio/Montana State
University; 59t,b © Carlos Goldin/SPL; 60l © Richmond
Marine Fossil Museum; 60r Queensland Museum/Jeff Wright;
63l © Tom & Patricia Rich; 63r © Peter Menzel/SPL; 66 ©
Canterbury Museum, NZ/Dr Norton Hiller; 67t,b © Dinosaur
Kingdom, Nakasato 72, 73t © Dutheil Didier/Corbis Sygma;
73b © Bobby Yip/Reuters/Corbis; 76 © Geological Museum of
China/NHMPL; 85r © Dr B. Booth/GeoScience Features PL;
89t,b © Dinópolis, Teruel, Spain; 90b © Dalian Natural
History Museum, China/David Varricchio

Every effort has been made to ensure the reproduction of content has
been done with the consent of the copyright owners. If you are aware
of any unintentional omissions, please contact the publishers directly
so that any necessary corrections may be made in future editions.

Contents

Callum Scott

The legacy of the dinosaurs

NOBODY IN THE WORLD HAS EVER SEEN a real live dinosaur. All the dinosaurs have died out – they've become extinct. The last ones disappeared 65 million years ago – that's more than 60 million years before there were any people in the world! So why are we fascinated by dinosaurs? Why do these beasts of the past grip our imagination?

Long-dead creatures such as Tyrannosaurus have become more famous than many creatures living today. People flock to see their remains in museums all around the world.

Big, fierce and fast

There are lots of reasons why dinosaurs are so exciting. Some were giants – by far the largest creatures ever to walk the Earth. Some were truly fearsome, with teeth like carving knives and mouths big enough to swallow humans whole. Some dinosaurs could run as fast as today's speedy ostriches. Others had such tough skin they looked like living suits of armour. People are constantly making new dinosaur discoveries. Dinosaurs may be long gone, but they regularly surprise us.

The dinosaur hunters

Dinosaurs are so fascinating that some people devote their lives to finding out more about them. These people are the dinosaur hunters. Of course, they will never meet a living dinosaur. What they seek are fossils – bones, teeth and other remains that have been preserved in the rocks over millions of years and turned to stone.

A lifelong passion

For professional fossil experts, known as palaeontologists, the quest for dinosaurs is a full-time job. For others it becomes a lifelong hobby as they spend every spare moment searching for fossils. Many people find very little. But some strike lucky. They may discover the fossils of a new kind of dinosaur or exciting clues about how dinosaurs lived and died. A few people even have dinosaurs named after them. This is one way to make your name live on and on!

Excavating fossils is a slow and difficult task. Dinosaur hunters may spend long weeks chipping away at rocks in the glaring sun or bitter wind.

Artists' impressions, such as this one of Anchiceratops, build on fossil information to help us visualise how the dinosaurs would have looked in real life.

PART ONE
The dinosaur world

PICTURE THE WORLD WITH NO PEOPLE AND therefore no roads, buildings, bridges or fields. When the dinosaurs lived, Earth was untouched by humans. Plants, animals and the land itself were very different, too.

The ancient Earth

Earth began about 4,500 million years ago. Scientists divide its immense history into huge time spans called eras. The Precambrian Era came first, lasting until 540 million years ago. Living things were tiny and simple, found only in the sea. Next came the Palaeozoic Era, or 'Ancient Life', from 540 to 250 million years ago. New plants and animals appeared, including fish such as sharks, and the first land creatures.

This is how the world might have looked when the dinosaurs first appeared. No grass grew on the rocky, open landscape – nor were there any flowering plants.

TRIASSIC | JURASSIC

250 240 230 220 210 200 190 180 170

The 'Age of Dinosaurs'

The Mesozoic Era, or 'Middle Life', lasted from 250 to 65 million years ago. Dinosaurs first came into existence near its beginning and died out at its end. So the Mesozoic Era is broadly the 'Age of Dinosaurs'. It is split into three smaller time spans – the Triassic Period, the Jurassic Period and the Cretaceous Period. Different kinds of dinosaurs came and went through all these times. Some small mammals, and later the first birds, joined them. But dinosaurs ruled the land for more than 150 million years.

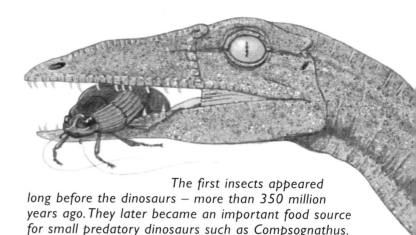

The first insects appeared long before the dinosaurs – more than 350 million years ago. They later became an important food source for small predatory dinosaurs such as Compsognathus.

After the dinosaurs

After the Mesozoic Era came the Cainozoic (Cenozoic) Era, or 'Recent Life', from 65 million years ago to the present. This is when mammals and birds took over from the dinosaurs. People have been around for little more than two million years. So, in comparison to the dinosaurs, we have inhabited Earth for a very short time.

Varied remains

Dinosaurs were not the only creatures to be preserved in the form of fossils. There are also fossils of other animals, from flies and fish to whales and mammoths – and of plants, such as trees and ferns. These varied fossils are often found alongside dinosaur remains. Experts use them to build up a picture of the landscape and wildlife of prehistoric times. Usually it is the hardest parts of a living thing that are preserved. For dinosaurs, these were teeth, bones, horns, claws and, very occasionally, skin.

Coelophysis was one of the earliest known dinosaurs, living about 225 to 220 million years ago. This is a Coelophysis skeleton, preserved as a fossil.

7

CRETACEOUS

150 140 130 120 110 100 90 80 70

The Triassic Period

THE TRIASSIC WAS THE FIRST PERIOD OF THE Mesozoic Era, lasting from 250 to 203 million years ago. Dinosaurs appeared part-way through it – about 230 million years ago. By the end of the period, dozens of kinds of dinosaurs roamed the world.

The changing map

Throughout Earth's history the main land-masses, or continents, have moved. They have drifted around very slowly, and they continue to move today. In Triassic times most of the land-masses were joined, forming one giant 'super-continent' called Pangaea. This was surrounded by a massive 'super-ocean' – Panthalassa.

Triassic climate

In the Triassic Period the climate was mainly warm and dry. Around the coasts of Pangaea there were some clouds and periods of rain. But these rarely reached the middle of the super-continent. Inland there were vast areas of dry rock, sand and desert.

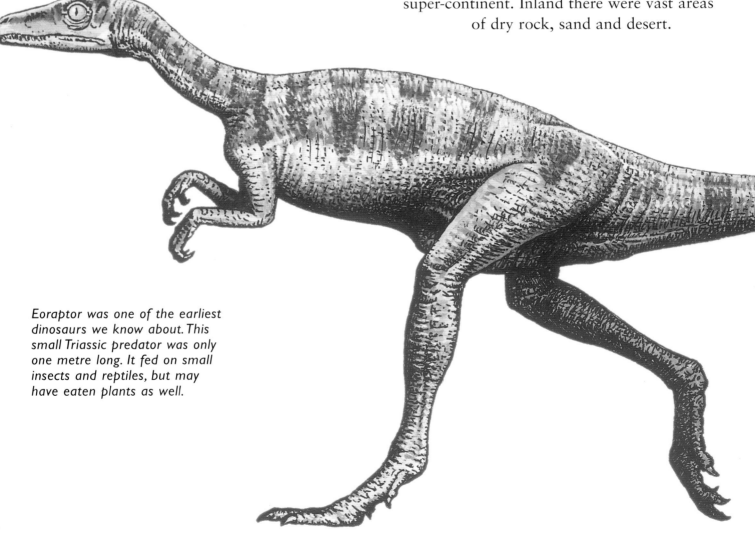

Eoraptor was one of the earliest dinosaurs we know about. This small Triassic predator was only one metre long. It fed on small insects and reptiles, but may have eaten plants as well.

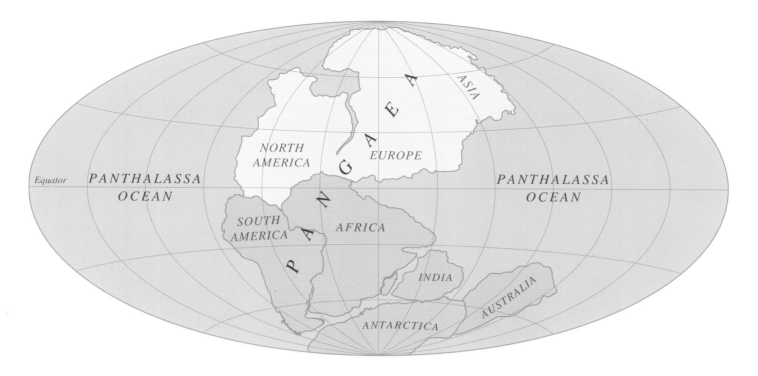

Plants of Triassic times

The main large plants of the Triassic Period were conifer trees and gingkoes (maidenhair trees). Cycads, resembling stumpy palm trees, were also common, as were tree-like seed-ferns.

All of these grew mainly around the edges of Pangaea – few plants could survive the dryness far inland. When rare rain did fall in central parts, short plants such as ferns, mosses and spiky horsetails sprang up in the damp ground.

Triassic animals

Dinosaurs, with their scaly skin, belonged to the reptile group. But they were not the first reptiles – many other kinds appeared earlier in the Triassic Period. Plant-eating reptiles included

The vast Panthalassa Ocean covered two-thirds of the Earth's surface. Some of the land that exists today was under water in prehistoric times.

pig-sized rhynchosaurs and hippo-like dicynodonts. There were also meat-eaters, similar to large lizards, that sprinted around on two back legs. These could have been the ancestors of the dinosaurs. Other meat-eaters were dog-like cynodonts, with sharp teeth and furry skin. They were probably ancestors of the mammals.

New shapes in the sky

As the dinosaurs came into being, so did another group of amazing creatures – the pterosaurs. They had beak-shaped mouths, furry bodies, and narrow wings of very thin skin, held out by long finger bones. They were the first large flying creatures. Different kinds of pterosaurs survived for as long as the dinosaurs – to the end of the Mesozoic Era.

CRETACEOUS

150 140 130 120 110 100 90 80 70

Triassic swamps

Triassic dinosaurs, like this plateosaur, lived mainly in wetlands near the coasts of Pangaea. Plateosaurs were probably the earliest large plant-eating dinosaurs, growing up to about ten metres long.

TRIASSIC

JURASSIC

250

240

230

220

210

200

190

180

170

The Jurassic Period

THE JURASSIC PERIOD LASTED FROM 203 to 135 million years ago. As it began, dinosaurs were becoming widespread, but the land-mass of Pangaea had started to split in two. The world's climate changed, and so all life on Earth was affected.

Wetter conditions

As the continents shifted, sea levels rose and the world became wetter. There were no proper seasons – it was warm and rainy almost everywhere, all the time. Many desert areas gave way to lakes, rivers, marshes and swamps. Great forests grew up, thriving in the damp conditions. Between them flourished smaller plants such as ferns, cycads, mosses and horsetails.

Different dinosaurs

The lush Jurassic greenery provided food for many plant-eaters, or herbivores. Some became vast in size. Giant dinosaurs such as Cetiosaurus (see page 28) had long necks so they could eat the leaves of tall trees. They may have reared up on their back legs for extra height. Some of the meat-eaters, or carnivores, were also large – for example Megalosaurus (see page 32). These beasts hunted the huge herbivores. Other dinosaurs stayed small and slim. Their main defence against predators was to run and hide.

Gasosaurus was a medium-sized Jurassic carnivore, about four metres long and two metres high. It had sharp teeth for tearing flesh, and strong back legs for running.

TRIASSIC

JURASSIC

250 240 230 220 210 200 190 180 170

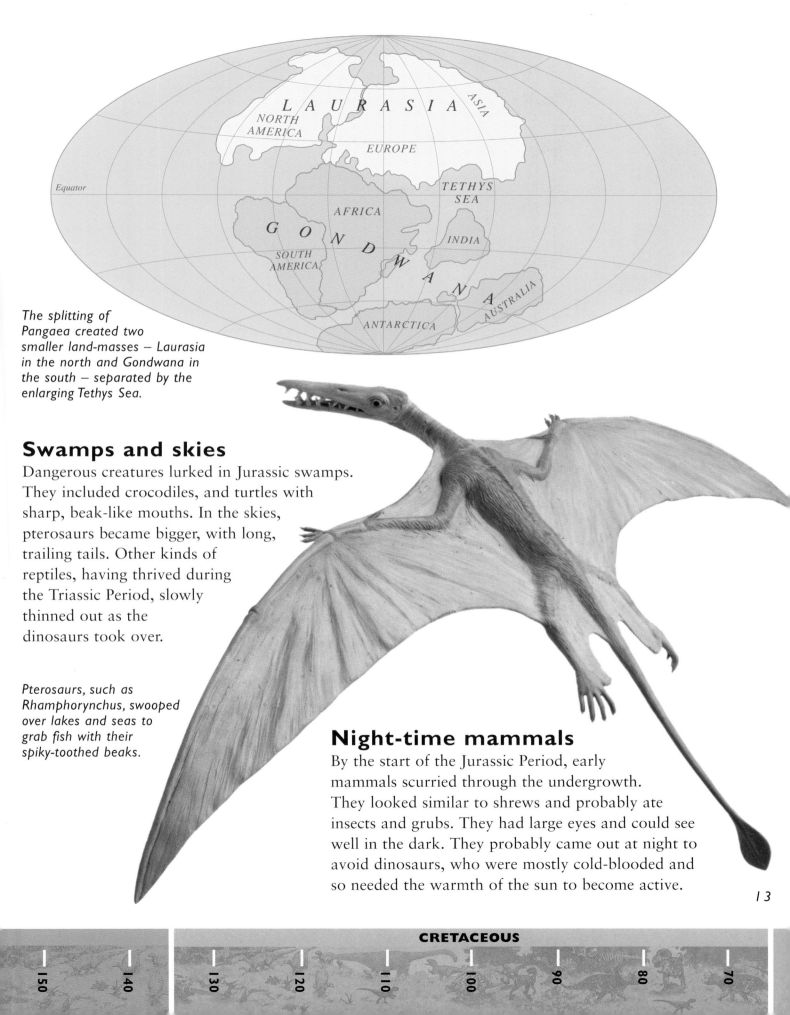

The splitting of Pangaea created two smaller land-masses – Laurasia in the north and Gondwana in the south – separated by the enlarging Tethys Sea.

Swamps and skies

Dangerous creatures lurked in Jurassic swamps. They included crocodiles, and turtles with sharp, beak-like mouths. In the skies, pterosaurs became bigger, with long, trailing tails. Other kinds of reptiles, having thrived during the Triassic Period, slowly thinned out as the dinosaurs took over.

Pterosaurs, such as Rhamphorynchus, swooped over lakes and seas to grab fish with their spiky-toothed beaks.

Night-time mammals

By the start of the Jurassic Period, early mammals scurried through the undergrowth. They looked similar to shrews and probably ate insects and grubs. They had large eyes and could see well in the dark. They probably came out at night to avoid dinosaurs, who were mostly cold-blooded and so needed the warmth of the sun to become active.

13

CRETACEOUS

150   140   130   120   110   100   90   80   70

Forest feasts

Jurassic herbivores, such as the giant, long-necked Brachiosaurus, small, sharp-toothed Elaphrosaurus and big, spiky Kentrosaurus, had a wealth of vegetation to feed on. Common trees included gingkoes, conifers such as Chilean pines (monkey puzzles), and giant sequoias (redwoods).

14

TRIASSIC

JURASSIC

250   240   230   220   210   200   190   180   170

CRETACEOUS

150   140   130   120   110   100   90   80   70

Forests everywhere

The climate stayed mild and damp to the end of the Jurassic Period. Forests became larger and trees grew taller. Cycads and seed-ferns also thrived, as did ferns, mosses and horsetails. However, there were still no flowering plants, so the world was mainly green and brown in colour.

The giant dinosaurs

Many of the biggest dinosaurs lived during the late Jurassic Period. They were plant-eaters, known as sauropods. A typical sauropod had a small head, a very long neck, a huge, barrel-shaped body, thick legs and a long, whippy tail. Brachiosaurus, Apatosaurus and Diplodocus were all sauropods. Another group of plant-eaters were the stegosaurs, whose bony back plates helped protect them from predators. Preying on these giants were fearsome carnivores such as Allosaurus and Yangchuanosaurus.

Other creatures

Late Jurassic mammals were smaller than today's pet cats and they stayed hidden for much of the time. Reptiles included tortoises and lizards – easy prey for hungry dinosaurs. Snakes had not yet appeared. There were plenty of insects such as dragonflies and cockroaches, but bees and butterflies would not arrive until later.

The first known bird, Archaeopteryx, developed about 150 million years ago. It was a strange mixture of reptile and bird – on its body were wings and feathers, but it also had teeth and a long, bony reptilian tail.

Left: Archaeopteryx was about the size of a crow and could fly quite well.

Right: A herd of Apatosaurus dine on a forest of monkey puzzle trees, overlooked by Ceratosaurus – a meat-eater with eyebrow 'horns'.

TRIASSIC

JURASSIC

250 240 230 220 210 200 190 180 170

CRETACEOUS

150   140   130   120   110   100   90   80   70

The Cretaceous Period

THE THIRD AND LAST PERIOD OF THE 'AGE of Dinosaurs' was the Cretaceous, lasting from 135 to 65 million years ago. It was a time of great change. The main land-masses continued to split, and very slowly the resulting continents drifted away from each other.

Changing seas

Sea levels rose and fell over many thousands of years during the Cretaceous Period. This meant that the outlines of the continents often changed, and lowland areas sometimes became vast, shallow seas. Living in the warm water were billions of small shellfish and other creatures.

Varied life

With the changing world came more varied dinosaurs. Iguanodon (see pages 38–39) was one of the most common plant-eaters, roaming the land in great herds. Some of the massive sauropods still survived, and a few became even bigger than their Jurassic relations. Various armoured dinosaurs, known as ankylosaurs, also plodded around.

In the air, pterosaurs were developing, too. They lost their trailing tails, and their beaks became longer and narrower. A few kinds of mammals started to grow larger. Repenomamus gigantus, for example, resembled a small bear – it probably fed on young dinosaurs.

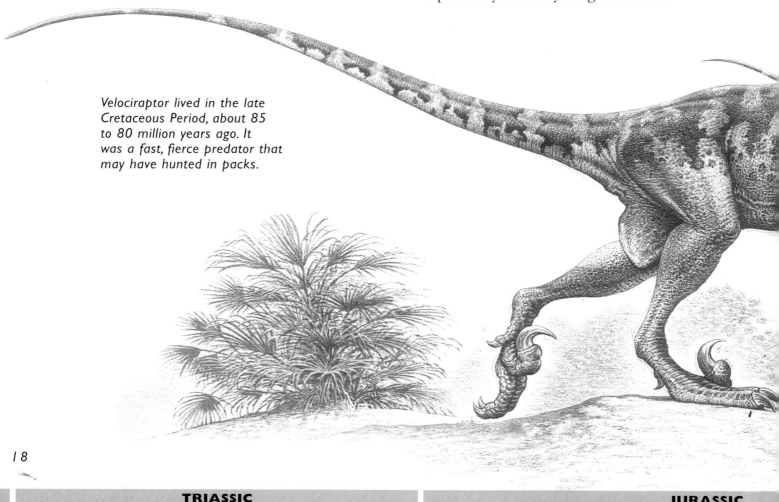

Velociraptor lived in the late Cretaceous Period, about 85 to 80 million years ago. It was a fast, fierce predator that may have hunted in packs.

TRIASSIC

JURASSIC

250 240 230 220 210 200 190 180 170

During the Cretaceous Period, Laurasia and Gondwana separated into smaller islands. Gradually they started to form the continents we know today.

Late-comers

Several new dinosaur groups appeared later in the Cretaceous Period. Ostrich-dinosaurs, such as Gallimimus, were the fastest land animals of the time. Ceratopsians, including Triceratops (see page 42), had horned faces and bony frills around their necks. Also new were strange-looking duck-billed dinosaurs, or hadrosaurs, such as Parasaurolophus (see page 20).

Breaking records

Two dinosaur record-holders lived during the Cretaceous Period. The plant-eater Argentinosaurus (see page 59) was possibly the biggest of all the dinosaurs and the largest land animal ever. It could have been more than 35 metres long and up to 100 tonnes in weight. In the same region (now South America) lived Giganotosaurus – the biggest known meat-eater (see page 59). At 14 metres and eight tonnes, it was even larger than the famous Tyrannosaurus.

CRETACEOUS

150 140 130 120 110 100 90 80 70

Climate and plants

The Cretaceous climate was less consistently damp than in Jurassic times. Rainfall became more scattered. In some regions, seasons started to emerge – warm, dry summers and cool, wet winters. Gradually these became more marked, sometimes bringing droughts or snow.

The changing conditions affected plant life. Great forests of conifers, gingkoes and cycads still stood, but new kinds of plants also appeared. These had flowers or blooms. At first they were small and weedy, but they gradually spread, dotting the landscape with patches of colour. Some plants, for example water lilies, spread into water. Others grew into shrubs and small trees, such as magnolias, maples, walnuts and oaks. Their leaves, blossoms, seeds and fruits were new food sources for animals – including the dinosaurs.

Flying creatures

With the spread of flowers came more insects. Bees buzzed and butterflies flitted. In the skies, pterosaurs grew even larger. The last types – such as Quetzalcoatlus – were the biggest flying animals of all time, with wings spanning 15 metres across. There were also many different kinds of birds. Some dived into the water to hunt fish, while others fed on the new flowers and their seeds.

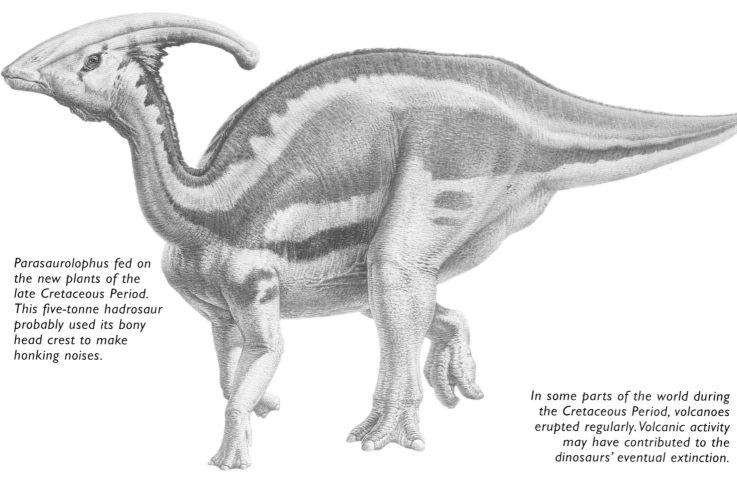

Parasaurolophus fed on the new plants of the late Cretaceous Period. This five-tonne hadrosaur probably used its bony head crest to make honking noises.

In some parts of the world during the Cretaceous Period, volcanoes erupted regularly. Volcanic activity may have contributed to the dinosaurs' eventual extinction.

TRIASSIC

JURASSIC

250 240 230 220 210 200 190 180 170

CRETACEOUS

150   140   130   120   110   100   90   80   70

TRIASSIC

JURASSIC

250

240

230

220

210

200

190

180

170

Out with a bang

The Cretaceous Period ended with a worldwide disaster. All the dinosaurs were wiped out, as were the pterosaurs and many large sea reptiles. Various types of shellfish and plants also disappeared. The reasons for this mass extinction are not clear. But most scientists believe that an asteroid (a giant lump of rock from space) may have smashed into the Earth. This would have caused tidal waves, earthquakes and volcanic eruptions, with dust and debris filling the skies and blocking out sunlight. The world would have been plunged into freezing darkness for months or even years, making life impossible for most plants and animals.

The survivors

Amazingly, several groups of animals lived through the global disaster. These included crocodiles, snakes, turtles, birds and mammals. Their survival is still a puzzle for scientists. However, the death of the dinosaurs – the largest and most ferocious animals ever to walk the Earth – meant that gradually these newer species flourished.

Left: A group of Troodon watch an approaching desert sandstorm. Clouds of choking dust would have been a huge danger to the dinosaurs.

Right: Some dinosaurs, such as these pinacosaurs, died in 'death huddles'. Perhaps they were trying to shelter from the dust.

PART TWO
Discovering the dinosaurs
A brief history of fossil hunting around the world

FOSSIL STUDY BEGAN SERIOUSLY IN EUROPE IN THE 1700s. But it wasn't until the 1830s that experts identified the dinosaurs as a group, separate from their reptilian relatives. It was even later that the group was given its own name – the Dinosauria (see page 34).

Dinosaurs rise to fame

Once people realised that certain fossils were the remains of huge, mysterious, extinct reptiles, interest rose. From the 1840s, some scientists

Muttaburrasaurus was a mid-Cretaceous herbivore, about seven metres long. Its first fossils were found in 1963 near the town of Muttaburra in central Queensland, Australia.

in Europe began to specialise in the study of dinosaurs, and in the 1850s dinosaurs began their rise to wider fame. The general public were soon marvelling at the first life-sized models of these huge and frightening beasts.

The trail goes west

In the second half of the 19th century, people in North America started looking for dinosaur fossils. From the 1860s, great expeditions led to exciting discoveries in the remote American Midwest. In the 1870s to 1890s, fossil hunters found and named more than 100 kinds of dinosaur, as well as hundreds of other prehistoric creatures. Later the trail spread to Canada, and many more wonderful fossils were unearthed.

Worldwide coverage

Fossil hunting in Africa, then in Central Asia (Mongolia) and in East Asia (China), caught on in the 1900s. Fresh finds were made during the 1960s in South America and Australia. By this time more than 600 kinds of dinosaur were known. In the 1990s, Chinese experts found yet more remarkable fossils, not only of dinosaurs but also of their very close relatives, the birds.

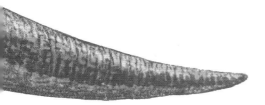

The search continues

Today fossil hunters are at work in almost every part of the world. They uncover dinosaur remains in nearly every region, even the icy poles. Each discovery adds to the mass of knowledge about how these great creatures lived, fed, bred and died. Old theories may be replaced with new ones – but then a fresh find might reverse ideas again. The exhilarating quest for dinosaurs continues at gathering speed.

Most new dinosaur fossils are found by large groups of people organised by museums, colleges, universities and research centres. The 'hunters' may include both experts and amateurs.

Hobby hunters

Almost anyone can take part in a fossil expedition. Many dinosaur hunters are untrained people who volunteer to try their luck, or who like a holiday with a difference. Amateur fossil fans may also make great finds while out walking in the countryside.

Strange old stones

Fossil finds in ancient times

ALTHOUGH SCIENTISTS HAVE STUDIED FOSSILS for only a few hundred years, people have been curious about these strangely shaped stones since ancient times. Fossils were found scattered on the ground or sticking out of rocks, but no one really knew what they were.

Unknown animals

The ancient world was by our standards a mysterious place – people did not have the scientific knowledge we have today. When they came upon fossil remains such as teeth, bones, horns and claws, they noticed the similarity to the same parts in living animals. But most people did not understand about fossilisation. They did not suspect that the remains were actually millions of years old. Instead, many assumed that the fossils came from giant creatures whose kind were still alive.

Monsters galore

Tales spread of huge beasts and fierce monsters hiding in forests, valleys and mountain-tops. These stories were repeated so often that for generations people believed they were true. In Europe, for example, the winged dragon is a popular character in folklore and fairytales.

The mythical dragon, such as this one from the legend of St George, had scaly skin, horns, sharp teeth and a long tail. If we take away its wings and fire-breathing power, it is not unlike some of the dinosaurs.

In modern times people have explored every region of Europe. No trace of dragons has been found, so we know they don't exist. But people long ago did not have this information.

Gods and spirits

Some people believed that the oddly shaped stones were nothing to do with real animals. Their idea was that the rocks were fashioned by the natural forces of wind, water and weather. Or perhaps they were made by gods and spirits, or by magical powers. Why should gods and spirits want to create such items? People invented reasons and explanations, and so more myths and legends began.

Dragon magic

In China, dragons are regarded as powerful protectors that ward off evil spirits and symbolise happiness and well-being. There is a long tradition of using 'dragon bones' for medicines that still continues today. The 'bones' are the fossils of dinosaurs, mammoths and other long-dead creatures. They are ground into powder, mixed with other substances such as herbs, and used as potions to treat a wide range of illnesses.

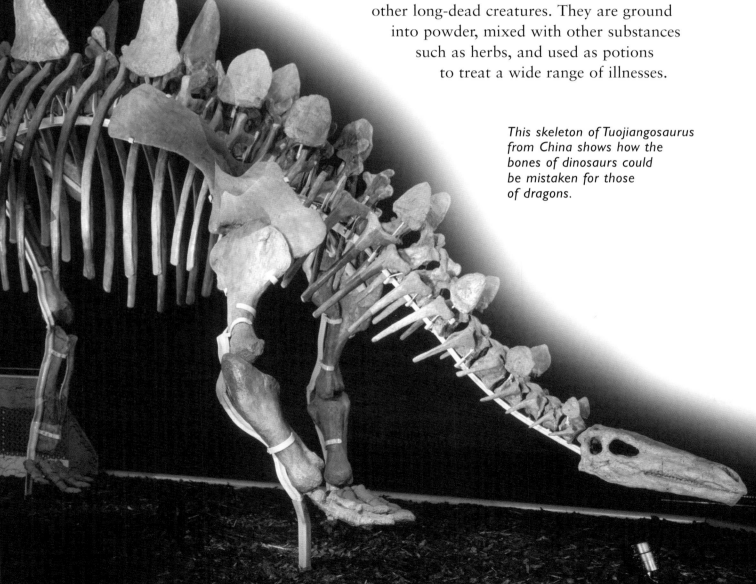

This skeleton of Tuojiangosaurus from China shows how the bones of dinosaurs could be mistaken for those of dragons.

Mythical monsters

Legends from across the globe

THERE ARE STORIES OF DINOSAUR-LIKE creatures from almost every part of the world. Yet the people who first told them probably had no knowledge of dinosaurs. Without the benefit of modern science, it seems amazing that their descriptions so closely match what we now know of prehistoric animals.

Legends from Europe

The French city of Nerluc was named after a horned 'dragon' supposedly killed there. Its descriptions sound very much like a Triceratops-type dinosaur. Fossilised dinosaur footprints in the Rhine Valley of Germany may have inspired the legend of Siegfried slaying the dragon, celebrated in the famous opera by Richard Wagner. Scottish tales tell of the Loch Ness Monster, similar to a sea-dwelling plesiosaur. In Ireland, the Sraheens Lough Monster resembles the bounding dinosaur Coelophysis. And in England, the Belua – a Tyrannosaurus-like hunter – is said to have gulped down Mordivus, King of the Britons, in AD 336.

African myths

In Kenya, the Muhuru is a legendary animal that looks like a stegosaur. There are also tales of a sail-backed giant lizard, similar to the extinct reptile Dimetrodon (which was not a dinosaur but lived earlier). Deep in the Likoala Swamp, in Congo, lurks the mythical Mokele-Mbembe, a creature similar to a long-necked, long-tailed sauropod such as Diplodocus.

Tales from Australia

Australians speak of the Burrunjor and Arnhem Rex, both creatures similar to Tyrannosaurus. Also famed in the Antipodes is the sauropod-like Kulta, which according to aboriginal legend lived in the swamps that once covered central Australia. The legendary Gauarge, a 'featherless emu', also from Australia, is similar to an ostrich-dinosaur such as Gallimimus.

Asian monsters

Nepalese people tell of the Buru – a five-metre-long reptile with four large teeth, a triangular head, big claws, and a strong tail with spikes sticking up from it. China's leathery-winged mythical creatures, ten metres across, seem very similar to pterosaurs, as does the New Guinea

Many descriptions of mythical monsters closely match modern images of sauropods such as Cetiosaurus. Measuring about 18 metres in length, Cetiosaurus lived in the middle Jurassic Period. Its fossils have been found in England and Morocco.

Ropen – a flying creature with a wingspan of about one metre and a long tail. New Guinea's 'furry lizards' show features of dinosaurs known as therizinosaurs or 'scythe-claws'.

Stories from the Americas

In Texas, USA, the legendary Mountain Boomer of the Big Bend region resembles a small, fierce, agile predator such as Velociraptor. American stories also tell of the raptor-like Colorado River Lizard, which is about one metre long and runs upright on its rear legs.

People of the Amazon region in South America talk of the Madidi Monster or Beni Swamp Beast, a creature like a sauropod. Also in legends from the Amazon are pterosaur-like flying creatures with wings six metres across, while Bolivian tales include a large meat-eating monster that seems similar to the dinosaur Allosaurus.

Allosaurus was a great carnivore, almost as big as Tyrannosaurus. Its teeth were the size of carving knives and just as sharp. Allosaurus fossils have been found in North America, Africa and Australia. Ancient tales of Allosaurus-like monsters are known from almost every continent.

In 1922, country folk in Argentina reported sightings of this huge plesiosaur-like beast. An expedition was planned from Buenos Aires, but the monster was never found.

29

The quest begins

Europe in the 18th century

IN ENGLAND IN THE 1700s, MANY RICH PEOPLE began collecting 'treasures of nature' to display in their grand houses. As well as flowers, insects and birds, these included fossils. Initially they were gathered more as curiosities than as specimens for study. But gradually scientists took an interest, too.

The problem of extinction

Most people in 18th-century Europe were Christians with very strong faith. They believed that God created the world and all living things in it, and that God would not allow any kinds of animals or plants to die out. If fossils were the remains of dead creatures, then those creatures must be earlier versions of species that still exist.

The Biblical story of Noah and the Ark helped most people to accept the idea of extinction. They came to believe that after the Great Flood, new life forms were created to populate the Earth, while the old species were preserved as fossils.

The Meuse monster

In 1770, a discovery in a Dutch chalk mine started to change these ideas. Miners uncovered the fossilised skull, jaws and teeth of a huge 'sea monster'. For many years people argued about these remains. Then they were examined by a leading animal expert, Georges Cuvier (1769–1832). The fossils were very different from any creature still alive. So Cuvier suggested this type of animal had indeed become extinct. He called it Mosasaurus, meaning 'Meuse reptile', after the Meuse river region where it was found.

Drowned out

Cuvier also studied fossil mammoth bones. In 1799, he declared that these were different from the bones of modern elephants. Cuvier's work had far-reaching effects. Some scientists began to accept the view that many kinds of living things had died out long ago. To fit with religious beliefs, it was suggested that the extinctions had begun during the Great Flood of Noah's time, as described in the Bible. A total of seven floods were said to have wiped out many species, but each time they were replaced with new ones.

An early professional

Mary Anning (1799–1847) was one of the first professional fossil hunters. She lived in Lyme Regis in Dorset, south-west England, a region that is rich in fossils exposed as waves eat into the cliffs. Mary had a good eye for fossils. She gathered them and sold them to museums and private collectors. Her finds included sea reptiles such as ichthyosaurs and plesiosaurs. However, the rocks she searched were formed on the sea bed. Dinosaurs did not live in the sea, so their fossils were missing from Mary's finds.

Above: Mary Anning with her dog in the fossil-rich area of Dorset that is now known as the Jurassic Coast. Below: Plesiosaurs were sea reptiles with long necks, tubby bodies and four flippers for swimming.

The first three

England in the early 19ᵗʰ century

THE FIRST DINOSAUR TO BE GIVEN AN official scientific name was Megalosaurus – 'big reptile' – in 1824. Its fossils were found in England, as were those of the next two dinosaurs to be named. However, at the time no one classified these creatures as dinosaurs – the word dinosaur was not invented until later.

Giant jaw

Megalosaurus was found in a quarry at Stonesfield, near Oxford, in about 1815. It was described and named by William Buckland (1784–1856), a professor of geology at the University of Oxford. The main fossil was a piece of lower jaw bone. Looking at the teeth, Buckland realised that it came from a huge, meat-eating reptile and thought it might have been a very large type of lizard.

Beaten to it?

It is possible that a Megalosaurus fossil had been described more than 100 years before Buckland's study – by Robert Plot (1640–96) from Oxford's Ashmolean Museum. In 1677, Plot's book *Natural History of Oxfordshire* showed a fossil with a double bulge, resembling the lower end of a thigh bone. It was so large that Plot thought it might have been from a giant human, or even an elephant that had been brought to England by the Ancient Romans. But the bone could have belonged to Megalosaurus. Plot knew nothing about dinosaurs and did not name the fossil, which has since been lost.

This piece of lower jaw bone was the first dinosaur fossil to receive a scientific name – Megalosaurus. As in many meat-eaters, the teeth are well spaced and curve backwards towards the throat – this would have stopped struggling prey from escaping. The oldest, tallest teeth regularly fell out and small new ones grew from the jaw to replace them.

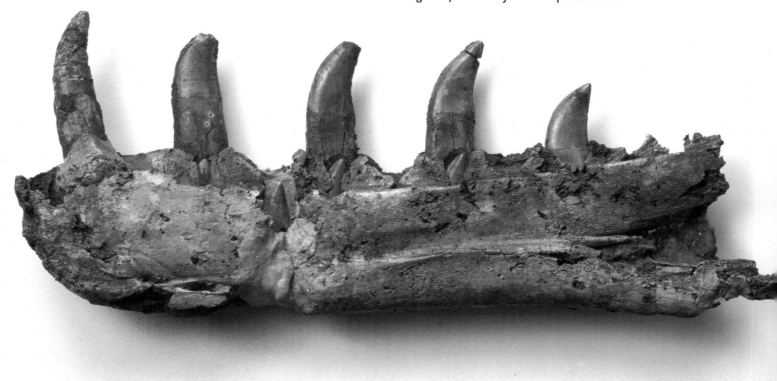

The fossil-finding doctor

Gideon Mantell was a doctor from Lewes in Sussex, southern England. In his spare time he explored the South Downs and collected all kinds of rocks and fossils, which he displayed in his home museum. Though an amateur, Mantell was the first well-known collector of dinosaur fossils.

Curious teeth

Around 1820–22, Mantell's wife, Mary, discovered some fossil teeth in a pile of gravel. Mantell was fascinated by their large size and peculiar shape. Some experts said they could be from a big fish, or even a recently dead rhinoceros. But Mantell knew that the rocks containing the teeth were much older. He also found that the teeth were shaped like those of an iguana lizard, although many times larger.

Introducing names

In 1825, Mantell's scientific report suggested that the teeth came from a huge, extinct, plant-eating lizard. He named it Iguanodon, meaning 'iguana tooth'. This was the second dinosaur to be given an official name. In 1833, Mantell described and named a third dinosaur. It was an armoured plant-eater called Hylaeosaurus, or 'woodland reptile', discovered in the Tilgate Forest area of Sussex.

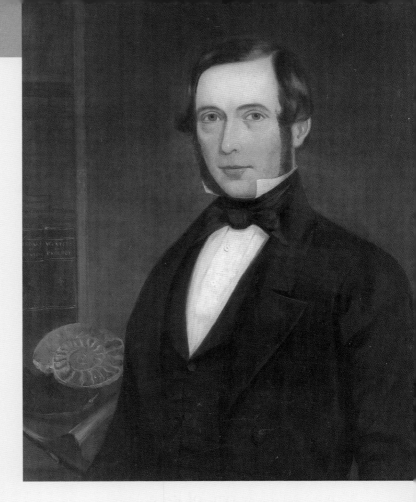

Gideon Mantell (1790–1852) introduced some of the first-ever dinosaur names. As well as Iguanodon and Hylaeosaurus, he also named the plant-eaters Pelorosaurus and Regnosaurus.

Reconstructions of the third dinosaur to be named – the four-metre-long Hylaeosaurus – are from very few fossils. In fact, this ankylosaur may be the same as the later-named Polacanthus (see pages 34–35).

The dinosaurs are named

England from 1842

THE WORD 'DINOSAUR' WAS INVENTED in England in 1842. English fossil expert Richard Owen decided that Megalosaurus, Iguanodon and Hylaeosaurus deserved their own reptile group. He named this the Dinosauria, meaning 'terrible reptiles'.

Public curiosity

During the 1840s, news of the dinosaurs reached the public. People wanted to know what these fearsome beasts looked like when they were alive. In 1850–51, a Great Exhibition was held in London's Hyde Park, inside an amazing glass building called the Crystal Palace. The building was then moved to Sydenham in south-east London. Between 1852 and 1854, Richard Owen worked with the sculptor Waterhouse Hawkins (1807–89) to construct life-sized models of various dinosaurs for the gardens of the Palace's new location.

Dinosaur fever

When the dinosaur models were put on show, they caused a sensation. People flocked from far and wide to gaze at them in awe. The reconstructions were not accurate by modern standards, because Owen and his colleagues lacked the detailed scientific knowledge we have today. But they started the first wave of 'dinosaur fever'. People began scouring the countryside, looking for dinosaur fossils – and a flood of new discoveries began.

Museum maestro

In 1856, Richard Owen took charge of the natural history collections at the British Museum in Central London. These included rocks, minerals, fossils, preserved plants, dead insects and stuffed animals. From 1880, Owen organised for the collections to be transferred a new building in South Kensington, south-west London. This is now the Natural History Museum. It houses one of the world's best collections of fossils from all kinds of animals and plants.

Richard Owen (1804–92) was an expert in anatomy (the structure of living things) as well as fossils.

Dinosaur dinner

In 1854, Owen and Hawkins hosted a special dinner party. About 20 fossil experts were invited, including William Buckland, Georges Cuvier and Gideon Mantell. They had their meal in the body of the part-built, life-sized Iguanodon, made for the Crystal Palace gardens. The glass building of the Crystal Palace was destroyed by fire in 1936, but the dinosaur models remain and are still a great attraction.

Throughout his career, Owen named various types of dinosaur, including the ankylosaur Polacanthus (below).

Interest across the Atlantic

North America in the 1850s

After the naming of the dinosaurs and the success of the Crystal Palace models, 'dinosaur fever' quickly spread across the Atlantic Ocean to North America. One of the first American experts to take an interest in the study of dinosaur fossils was Joseph Leidy.

A prominent professor

Joseph Leidy was professor of anatomy at the University of Pennsylvania. He preferred not to spend his days wandering in the wilds, collecting fossils. Usually people brought fossil specimens to him.

The first American dinosaurs

In the mid 1850s, Leidy named several new dinosaurs, all found in America. One was the small, speedy meat-eater Troodon (see page 22). There was also a bigger carnivore called Deinodon, which was similar to the English Megalosaurus. A third was the large duck-billed herbivore Trachodon, which Leidy thought was similar to Iguanodon. Leidy based these names on the evidence of few fossil remains – mainly teeth.

Clues from a quarry

In 1858, Leidy examined major new finds from part-time scientist William Foulke (1816–65). Foulke had heard that fossil bones had been found in a quarry in Haddonfield, New Jersey, about 20 years previously. The remains had been lost, so Foulke decided to look again. The quarry was by then no longer used, partly filled in and overgrown. But about three metres down, Foulke's team discovered a treasure trove of fossils from a huge creature, including teeth, backbones and leg bones.

Joseph Leidy (1823–91) became one of the most important early dinosaur hunters in North America.

This was the first dinosaur skeleton found in North America – a large, plant-eating duck-bill, about ten metres long. Leidy studied it and named it Hadrosaurus.

Changing ideas

The work of Foulke and Leidy greatly changed opinions of how dinosaurs looked in life. Finding limb bones allowed Leidy to 'rebuild' Hadrosaurus in a way that differed from models of the similar dinosaur Iguanodon back in England. As a result, Hadrosaurus was shown standing almost upright on its back legs, with front legs held forwards, like a kangaroo.

American Charles R. Knight (1874–1953) was one of the earliest dinosaur artists. This action-packed painting, from about 1898, shows a battle between two Dryptosaurus meat-eaters. Knight also created a model of the scene.

Sights in Central Park

In 1856, a large site in New York City was set aside amid the buildings and the bustle, to create Central Park. One of its early attractions in 1868 was a set of dinosaurs. They were life-sized models including Hadrosaurus and a six-metre-long predator now known as Dryptosaurus. The models were made by Waterhouse Hawkins, sculptor of the Crystal Palace collection. Unfortunately no trace of them remains today.

This Hadrosaurus was the first-ever dinosaur skeleton to be reassembled. It was mounted in New York in 1868, by the man pictured here – British sculptor Waterhouse Hawkins.

Mass grave in a mine

Belgium in the 1870s

IN EUROPE, THE QUEST FOR DINOSAURS WAS given an exciting boost in 1878. At the Sainte Barbe coalmine in the village of Bernissart, western Belgium, workers discovered a 'mass grave' of dinosaurs. It lay more than 300 metres below the surface, in a clay-filled crack that ran across the coal seam the miners were digging.

Extensive excavation

The Bernissart 'grave' consisted of 39 fossil skeletons of Iguanodon, some with just a few bones but others almost complete. The task of excavating the great discovery was taken over by Louis De Pauw (1844–1918) and the Royal Museum of Natural History in Brussels (now the Royal Institute of Natural Sciences).

As each skeleton was uncovered, detailed notes and drawings were made of its position, and it was given a letter for identification. The fossils were transported by mine wagons and hoisted to the surface, then sent to Brussels by rail. The whole process took about three years.

Rebuilding the fossils

At the museum, the fossils were carefully pieced back together in sections, just as they had been found in the mine. The best-preserved and most complete skeletons were chosen for careful reconstruction of Iguanodon, to show how it would have looked in life. In charge of this part of the work was Belgian fossil expert Louis Dollo (1857–91), assisted by De Pauw. In 1882, Dollo produced a report. He suggested that Iguanodon had an almost upright pose, like a kangaroo.

Displaying the fossils

The fossil Iguanodon skeletons from Bernissart were put on display at the Royal Institute of Natural Sciences in Parc Leopold, Brussels. Some were arranged as they were found lying in the mine. Others have been rebuilt in upright poses and grouped together as if they are a herd travelling on a journey. Some of the individuals measure ten metres from nose to tail-tip. In life each Iguanodon probably weighed four tonnes or more – about the same as a large elephant.

Dollo and his team reconstructed Iguanodon as they thought it would have stood in life. Compare this to the more recent artist's impression opposite.

The Iguanodon debate

Dollo's work matched the ideas of Joseph Leidy in America, but not the proposals of Gideon Mantell, Richard Owen and others in England. They had pictured Iguanodon as a giant lizard, with its body held low and level to the ground, and limbs sticking out to the sides. Modern scientists disagree with both these theories. Today Iguanodon is usually depicted with its body leaning forwards, neck stretched out in front and tail behind, with its four limbs directly below the body.

Iguanodon lived and travelled in large herds. Recent studies suggest it moved on four legs most of the time, but could also run just on its strong hind legs.

Dinosaur wars in the Wild West

North America in the 1870s to 1900s

IN 1877, A 'DINOSAUR GOLD RUSH' BEGAN IN North America. Two new fossil sites were discovered, rich in remains of dinosaurs and other creatures. Both were in Colorado – but they were excavated by two rival teams.

Parallel finds

The first site was near Cañon City, south-west of Colorado Springs, and was discovered by O.W. Lucas, a teacher and part-time fossil hunter. Lucas contacted palaeontologist Edward Drinker Cope (1840–97), who quickly arranged for the fossils to be excavated and studied.

The other site was a ridge near Morrison, south-west of Denver. Fossils here were found by Arthur Lakes who, like Lucas, was a part-time teacher and fossil enthusiast. Lakes decided to enlist the help of Othniel Charles Marsh (1831–99), a professor of palaeontology at Yale College. Marsh organised a team of explorers who went to recover the fossils.

Bitter rivals

The two Colorado events were an amazing coincidence, as Marsh and Cope were already great rivals. In about 1869, Cope had rebuilt the fossil skeleton of a type of plesiosaur called Elasmosaurus. Marsh had seen the skeleton on a visit, and noticed that Cope had put the head at the wrong end – on the tip of the tail. Marsh made sure the world knew about this mistake, and hence sparked a feud between the two experts that lasted for the rest of their lives.

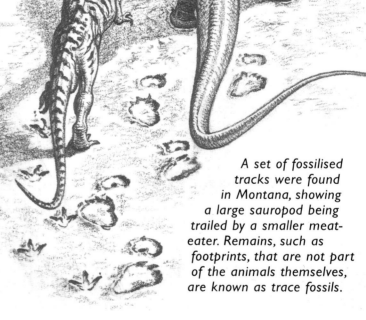

A set of fossilised tracks were found in Montana, showing a large sauropod being trailed by a smaller meat-eater. Remains, such as footprints, that are not part of the animals themselves, are known as trace fossils.

The 'Bone Wars'

By 1880, the rival teams of Marsh and Cope were digging in various sites in Montana, Wyoming and New Mexico. Their feud grew into the 'Bone Wars'. Members of one team would spy on the others, try to ruin their excavations, disrupt their supplies of food and water, and even smash each other's fossils or add fake ones to lead them astray.

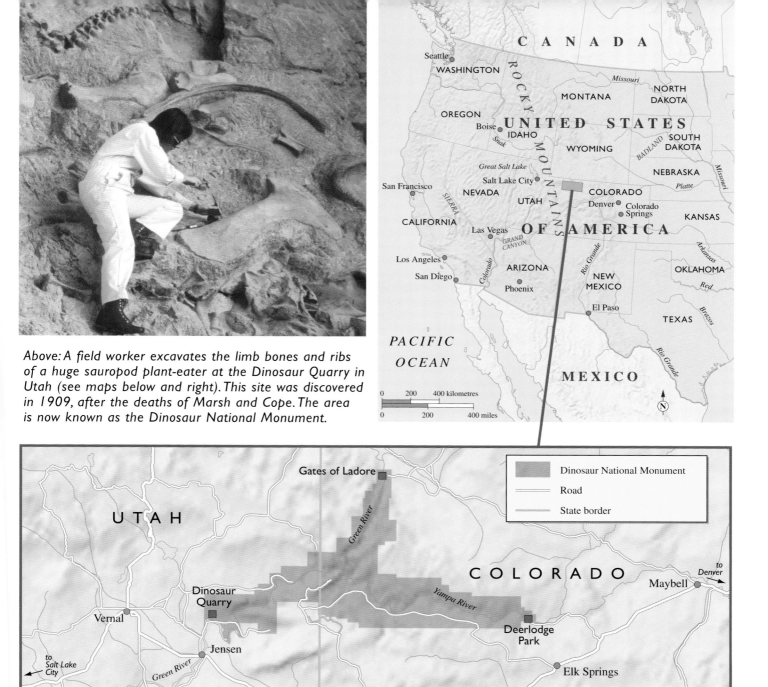

Above: A field worker excavates the limb bones and ribs of a huge sauropod plant-eater at the Dinosaur Quarry in Utah (see maps below and right). This site was discovered in 1909, after the deaths of Marsh and Cope. The area is now known as the Dinosaur National Monument.

A rush of new names

Cope and Marsh each rushed to describe and name more dinosaurs than the other. Between them, during the 1880s to 1890s, they named more than 130 new dinosaurs, plus hundreds of other fossil creatures. Some of this work was done in a hurry and certain names are no longer regarded as accurate. However, many others are.

Marsh's discoveries included the plant-eating dinosaurs Triceratops, Stegosaurus, Diplodocus and the massive Apatosaurus, as well as the big meat-eater Allosaurus. Cope named 1,000 creatures in his career, including dinosaurs such as the large sauropod Camarasaurus, the lightweight predator Coelophysis and the horned herbivore Monoclonius.

Discoveries on Red Deer River

Canada from the 1880s

DURING THE 1880S, NORTH AMERICAN dinosaur hunters crossed the border into Canada. The Red Deer River Valley in the province of Alberta was the location of many great fossil finds, beginning in 1884 with the skull of a fearsome meat-eater.

Changing ID
The skull was discovered by Joseph Tyrrell (1858–1957), who was working for the Geological Survey of Canada. At first it was identified by Edward Drinker Cope (see pages 40–41) as a specimen of the carnivore Laelaps. However, in 1905 Henry Fairfield Osborn (1857–1935), of the American Museum of Natural History, decided it was different

Albertosaurus was similar to Tyrannosaurus but smaller, at nine metres long and two tonnes in weight. It would have been a threat to herbivores such as Triceratops, which defended themselves with their pointy horns.

enough to be treated as a new kind of dinosaur. He named it Albertosaurus, after the province where it was found.

A floating base
In 1910, a second wave of fossil expeditions began along the Red Deer River. One of the all-time great dinosaur hunters led the trips – he was Barnum Brown (1879–1968), from the American Museum of Natural History. In such rocky, hilly country, wheeled vehicles were

useless. So Brown organised a large barge to travel along the Red Deer River, acting as a floating 'base camp' for teams of collectors. His fossil finds included the horned plant-eaters Anchiceratops (see page 5) and Leptoceratops, and the duck-billed hadrosaurs Corythosaurus, Kritosaurus and Saurolophus. Brown made expeditions all around the world and brought many fossils of dinosaurs and other creatures back to the museum in New York. Some of his greatest discoveries are still on display today.

Brown is remembered for discovering early specimens of Tyrannosaurus, such as this sacrum bone (part of the backbone) being excavated at Hell Creek, Montana, USA.

Fossil-hunting family

In 1912, the Sternberg family from Canada joined the Red Deer River hunt. Charles H. Sternberg (1850–1943) and his sons George (1883–1969), Charles M. (1885–1981) and Levi (1894–1976) made a barge and found a great series of remains. Charles H. worked out ways of protecting delicate, crumbly fossils in cases, or jackets. Charles M. continued to fossil-hunt for many years, and even by the 1950s was discovering dinosaurs such as the duck-bill Brachylophosaurus and the horned ceratopsian Pachyrhinosaurus. Levi devised techniques for copying fossils using rubbery latex casts.

The Tendaguru quarries

Africa in the 1900s

IN THE 1900S, ANOTHER CONTINENT CAME under the spotlight of the dinosaur hunters. In the Mtwara region of German East Africa (now mainly Tanzania) a huge series of massive fossils were found in an area of quarries known as the Tendaguru Formation.

The first finds

The first Tendaguru discoveries were made in 1907 by a German professor of palaeontology, Eberhard Fraas (1862–1915). Within a year, German scientists Edwin Hennig (1882–1977) and Werner Janensch (1878–1969), from the Berlin Museum of Natural History, had organised a great expedition.

The excavations at Tendaguru lasted for four years. They produced remains from one of the largest of all dinosaurs – the 70-tonne Brachiosaurus – as well as the spiked stegosaur Kentrosaurus and the fearsome meat-eater

Local people helped to carry the heavy fossil bones in slings from Tendaguru to Lindi, the nearest port.

Dicraeosaurus. Brachiosaurus fossils had already been unearthed in America's Grand River Valley, Colorado. But the Tendaguru finds were far more numerous and complete.

Difficult conditions

By the 1900s, fossil hunters were used to working in difficult conditions. They endured scorching days, cold nights, wearying winds and very few comforts in their remote camps. In the fierce heat and humidity of East Africa, there was also the risk of tropical diseases.

A lot of rock

At Tendaguru there were few roads and no railways. The massive fossils of Brachiosaurus and others had to be split into pieces and carried by people more than 65 kilometres to the local port. A single fossilised leg bone of Brachiosaurus, being solid rock, weighed a couple of tonnes. Over four years, more than 250 tonnes of fossils were transported from Tendaguru to Berlin for study.

Giant skeleton

At the museums in Berlin, the parts of the main Brachiosaurus find were cleaned from their surrounding rocks and pieced back together. The result was an immense skeleton almost 23 metres long. Brachiosaurus had long front legs and a giraffe-like neck, and its reconstruction stands a towering 12 metres tall – about the same height as a four-storey building.

In honour of Werner

Long after his death, Werner Janensch – like many famous fossil hunters – had a dinosaur named after him. The huge, long-necked plant-eater was called Janenschia. It measured about 25 metres from its nose to the tip of its lengthy tail, and weighed something like 25 tonnes. Its fossils come from East and South-East Africa.

Above: A single fossil leg bone from a sauropod is heavier than a person. Often – as with this humerus (upper 'arm' bone) from Torneria – lightweight copies are made from plaster or fibreglass resin for display in museums.

Left: Brachiosaurus, mounted at Berlin's Humboldt Museum, is the biggest dinosaur known from fairly complete remains.

45

Dinosaur desert

Mongolia in the 1920s

IT WAS NOT LONG BEFORE THE DINOSAUR QUEST reached the world's largest continent – Asia. In 1922, a large expedition, organised by the American Museum of Natural History, travelled to the dusty Gobi Desert of Mongolia.

Unexpected finds

The expedition's original aim was to find fossils of early human beings – 'missing links' in the evolution of our own kind from some type of ape-like ancestor. However, the rocks of the area were much too old for such remains. Instead they yielded a wealth of fossils of dinosaurs and other creatures, mostly from late Cretaceous times, 85 to 65 million years ago.

Expedition leaders

The expedition was led by three world-renowned dinosaur hunters – Roy Chapman Andrews (1884–1960), who later became director of the American Museum of Natural History, Henry Fairfield Osborn (1857–1935), president of the museum, and Walter Granger (1872–1941), the expedition's chief palaeontologist. Previously Granger had worked at a famous site called Bone Cabin Quarry in Wyoming, USA, where a shepherd had built a cabin-like shelter from the dinosaur fossils he had found lying around.

Harsh environment

Four expeditions were made into the Gobi from 1922 to 1925. Conditions were extremely harsh. Temperatures soared to 45°C by day, and plunged to -30°C at night. The relentless winds whipped up sandstorms and covered everything with fine dust. Water, food and other supplies were scarce. Transport was extremely difficult, with few landmarks or tracks in the vast wilderness, and local bandits were a threat.

Mongolian beasts

Despite having to struggle against adverse conditions, the Gobi fossil collectors were rewarded with exciting discoveries. One, Tarbosaurus, was a huge, fanged carnivore, very similar to Tyrannosaurus. In fact many experts today believe that Tyrannosaurus and Tarbosaurus were the same type of dinosaur.

Roy Chapman Andrews was an American naturalist and explorer. Here he examines some of his fossil finds from the Gobi, including the first recognised dinosaur eggs. The eggs were later identified as Protoceratops.

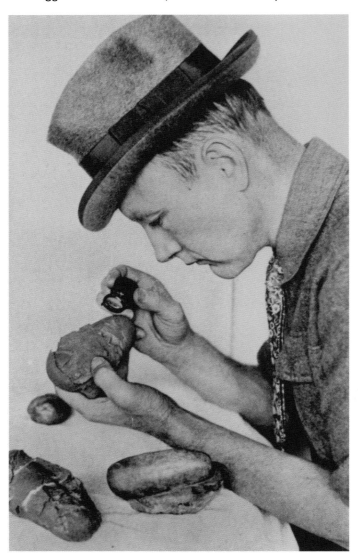

Protoceratops had to defend its nests from thieving predators such as Velociraptor.

Other discoveries included the agile dromaeosaur Velociraptor, and Pinacosaurus – an ankylosaur with a massive club of bone at the end of its tail, which it could swing like a hammer at enemies. A further find was thought to be the bird-like Oviraptor (see pages 48–49), though more recent discoveries suggest that these fossils were actually from its slightly smaller relation, Conchoraptor.

Nests and eggs

Some of the most startling discoveries in Mongolia were dinosaur nests containing eggs – all fossilised as rock. Fossilised dinosaur eggs had never been identified before. The sausage-shaped eggs were laid by the pig-sized horned dinosaur, Protoceratops. Each nest was a round, scooped-out bowl in the earth, with the eggs laid in a ring. In the area there were also bones of many Protoceratops, ranging in size from just-hatched babies to full-grown adults.

Riches of the wilderness

Some major Gobi finds

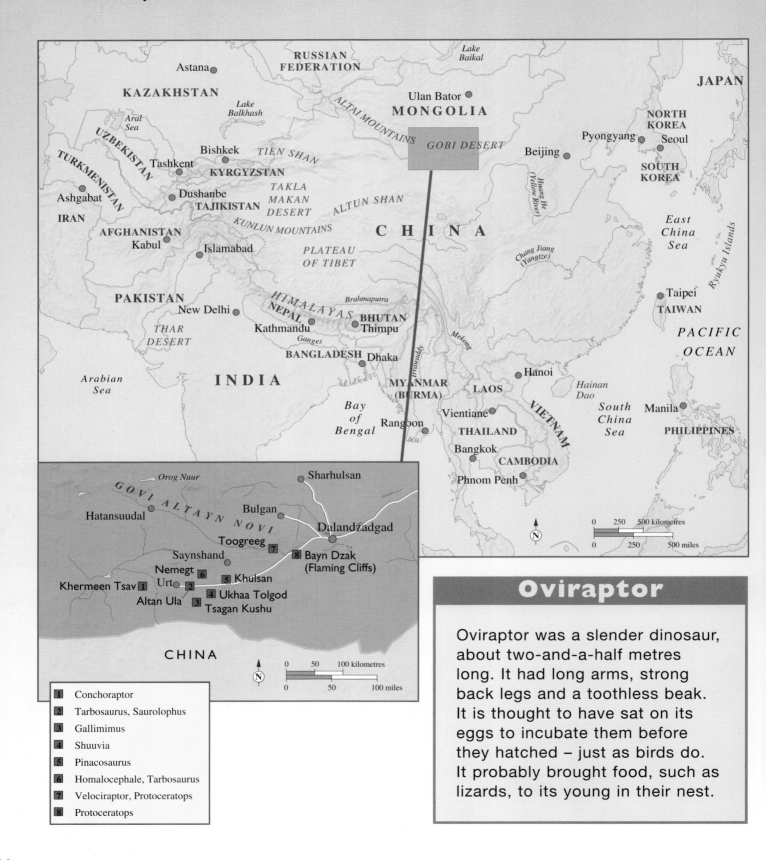

1 Conchoraptor
2 Tarbosaurus, Saurolophus
3 Gallimimus
4 Shuuvia
5 Pinacosaurus
6 Homalocephale, Tarbosaurus
7 Velociraptor, Protoceratops
8 Protoceratops

Oviraptor

Oviraptor was a slender dinosaur, about two-and-a-half metres long. It had long arms, strong back legs and a toothless beak. It is thought to have sat on its eggs to incubate them before they hatched – just as birds do. It probably brought food, such as lizards, to its young in their nest.

More than dragons

China in the early 20th Century

FOSSILS KNOWN LOCALLY AS 'DRAGON BONES' or 'dragon's teeth' have been found in China for centuries. They were initially used in traditional ceremonies, or ground into powders with supposed medical powers (see page 27). The first scientific studies of fossils were not carried out until the 20th century.

First finds

In 1915–17, Russian palaeontologists recovered dinosaur remains from sites in northern China and took them back to St Petersburg for study. One of the new discoveries from this work was a large plant-eater – a duck-bill, or hadrosaur. It was named Mandschurosaurus – 'Manchurian reptile' – and it came from late Cretaceous times, near the end of the Mesozoic Era.

The missing link?

In 1927, a fossil find in China made world headlines. But it was not the remains of a dinosaur. It was the tooth of a very ancient type of human. The fossil was found in

a site known locally as Dragon-Bone Hill, near the village of Zhoukoudian (Chou-K'ou-Tien), not far from Peking (now Beijing). People were excited that they had discovered the 'missing link' between apes and modern humans. They called it 'Peking Man'.

Further digging revealed the fossils of more than 40 individuals, along with stone tools, animal bones, and the remains of hearths with fires. For a time the news about 'ape-men' pushed dinosaurs into the background.

Mandschurosaurus was the first Chinese dinosaur to be named. It was about eight metres long and nearly five metres high.

A natural leader

During the 1920s, several groups of fossil hunters from Europe and North America joined major expeditions with Chinese palaeontologists to search for dinosaurs and other fossil creatures. They included teams from France and Sweden. However, the political situation in China meant that people from other countries were regarded with suspicion. It was difficult to arrange for permits to dig at sites.

Yang Zhong-Jian (1897–1979) led dinosaur digs and discoveries from 1933 until the late 1970s. He became known as the 'Father of Chinese Palaeontology'.

The eminent C.C. Young

From the mid 1930s, Chinese fossil hunters organised their own expeditions. One of their leaders was Yang Zhong-Jian (Young Chung Chien), known in Europe and America as 'C.C. Young'. He studied in Munich, Germany, and then returned to China to supervise many excavations at numerous sites. 'C.C.' remained one of China's greatest fossil experts for more than 50 years. In 1941, he named Lufengosaurus from fossils found in the Lufeng Basin of Yunnan province. Other discoveries included the plant-eating sauropod Omeisaurus – a massive 20 metres long – and the even longer-necked Mamenchisaurus (see page 52).

Lufengosaurus

The remains of Lufengosaurus included around 30 skeletons, in varying degrees of completion. Lufengosaurus was about

six metres long and weighed half a tonne, with a fairly long neck and tail. It was a member of the group called prosauropods, similar to the well-known Plateosaurus from Europe. Lufengosaurus lived in the early Jurassic Period some 200 million years ago.

Omeisaurus means 'Sacred Mountain Lizard' – it was named after Emei Mountain in China, where its first fossils were found. It lived in the late Jurassic Period.

Expansion in the East

China after 1949

IN 1949, CHINA ENTERED A PERIOD OF GREAT change as the People's Republic of China was founded. Digging for fossils was sometimes allowed and sometimes not. When expeditions did go ahead, fossil collectors visited an increasing range of sites.

Significant three

Three remarkable dinosaurs were among those unearthed in China during the 1950s to 1970s. Mamenchisaurus was a massive sauropod with an extra-long neck, named in 1954 after Mamen Brook in Sichuan where it was found.

The plant-eating Mamenchisaurus – the largest animal ever to be found in China – measured 24 metres from nose to tail. Its neck took up almost half of this length! Here it towers over the stegosaur Tuojiangosaurus.

The five-tonne Shantungosaurus, named in 1973 after the site of Shantung (Shangdong), was one of the biggest hadrosaurs. Tuojiangosaurus, found near the Tuo Jiang River in 1974, was a stegosaur with bony plates along its back.

A curious mix-up

The duck-billed dinosaurs, or hadrosaurs, are famed for their head crests – strange growths of hollow bone protruding from their skulls. In 1950, in Laiyang, a new hadrosaur was discovered and named Tsintaosaurus. Its head crest looked rather like the horn of a mythical unicorn. But further studies showed that this was probably a mistake. The 'horn' was a fossil from another animal, and the dinosaur without the horn is now known as Tanius.

'Mr Dinosaur'

From 1952, nearly all Chinese fossil studies and expeditions were organised by the Institute of Vertebrate Palaeontology and Palaeoanthropology (IVPP) in Beijing. The director there was the famous Yang Zhong-Jian, or 'C.C. Young' (see page 51). In 1962, he was joined by a young assistant called Dong Zhiming, who would soon become China's 'Mr Dinosaur'.

Rare rocks

In 1979, at a quarry near Dashanpu in Sichuan province, Dong found a 'dinosaur graveyard' with thousands of fossils. Many of them came from previously unknown types of dinosaur. The remains dated to the middle Jurassic Period, about 170 million years ago. This was a major discovery, because few sedimentary rocks (those that contain fossils) were laid down at that time, and so fossil finds of this age are rare.

Drowned in a flood

The area at Dashanpu was once a lake at the end of a river. During floods, the

Dong Zhiming (born 1937) leans on a model of a stegosaur. During his career he has discovered and named many dinosaurs.

drowned bodies of dinosaurs and other creatures washed along the river and then rotted on the lake shore. Gradually the mud and bones built up, as the flood returned year after year. Dong's team recovered remains of more than 100 dinosaurs, including the long-necked plant-eater Shunosaurus. In 1987, a dinosaur museum opened at the Dashanpu site, with displays of amazing 'bone beds' – large expanses of fossils lying jumbled in the rocks.

1 Lufengosaurus
2 Tuojiangosaurus
3 Mamenchisaurus
4 Dinosaur bone beds
5 Tanius
6 Psittacosaurus
7 Microraptor gui
8 Beipiaosaurus
  Sinosauropteryx
  Protarchaeopteryx
  Caudipteryx
  Sinornithosaurus

Cause for confusion

Africa in the 1960s to 1970s

OCCASIONALLY PALAEONTOLOGISTS FIND IT hard to tell whether their fossil finds come from new or already-named types of dinosaur. Confusion of this kind occurred in southern Africa when two separate expeditions visited Lesotho in the 1960s and 1970s.

Ginsberg and the jaw

The first expedition took place in 1964, unearthing part of a worn-down lower jaw. The bone was examined by palaeontologist Leonard Ginsburg, from the Museum of Natural History in Paris, France. He decided that it came from a small, slim, plant-eating dinosaur that lived during the early Jurassic Period. On the evidence of this one small fossil, Ginsburg called the dinosaur Fabrosaurus. The name honoured his colleague Jean Henri Fabre, who was a member of the expedition.

Galton's theory

In the 1970s, an English expedition from London's University College visited Lesotho. More remains were found of a similarly lightweight plant-eater, which was at first also thought to be Fabrosaurus. Then experts decided that the original Fabrosaurus fossil was too limited to confirm whether the new and much more complete remains were from the same kind of dinosaur. So, in 1978, the new find was renamed by the British-born palaeontologist Peter Galton. He called it Lesothosaurus, after the discovery region.

Shedding teeth?

The fossils of Lesothosaurus show two of them curled up together. Found nearby were worn teeth that could have been theirs. Perhaps the two went into a burrow to sleep through the dry season when plant food was lacking. While there, they lost or shed their teeth. New ones would grow later, as in various reptiles today.

French fossil expert Leonard Ginsburg – pictured here in the Paris Museum of Natural History – has long argued that climate change caused by falling sea levels wiped out the dinosaurs, not the impact of a huge asteroid.

Dinosaur naming dilemmas

The single fossil of Fabrosaurus is very similar to those of Lesothosaurus. Maybe they were the same kind of dinosaur. At present, there is not enough evidence to know. If further finds show that the two were the same kind, what would happen? The official rules say that the first name stays and any later ones go. So the name Lesothosaurus would be dropped and its fossils would be renamed Fabrosaurus.

A giant misunderstanding

This problem with naming fossils is nothing new. You may have heard of the dinosaur 'Brontosaurus', but actually the name was a mistake. In 1903, studies showed that Brontosaurus – a huge sauropod found in Wyoming, USA – was no different from the already-named Apatosaurus. Brontosaurus was therefore wiped from the official list.

Apatosaurus (pictured right) was named in 1877. Two years later, a similar skeleton was named Brontosaurus. But on further inspection it turned out that Brontosaurus and Apatosaurus were really the same type of dinosaur.

Mysterious prints

Since the 1970s, many sets of fossilised dinosaur footprints, or trackways, have been identified in Lesotho. Local people have long known about them and wondered about the creatures that once walked their land. The prints were made by a variety of dinosaurs, including small plant-eaters and larger sauropods. Most date from the early Jurassic period, about 200 million years ago. Some of the excavated tracks are now on display at Morija Museum in western Lesotho.

Northern Lesotho's Subeng Stream footprints are set in sandstone. They were probably made when dinosaurs walked across a sandbar at a bend in a slow river.

Excitement in Argentina

South America from the 1960s

FOSSILS HAD BEEN FOUND IN ARGENTINA SINCE the early 1900s. But some spectacular finds in the last decades of the 20th century helped to make South America, and especially Argentina, a focal spot for dinosaur hunting.

Miniature as mice

In 1979, fossil expert José Bonaparte (see right), with his colleague Martin Vince, studied and named the smallest dinosaurs known from fossils at the time. They were babies, just hatched from eggs, and in life would have been about the same size as rats today. The name given to them was Mussaurus, meaning 'mouse reptile'. Some of the babies were still curled in their eggs, unhatched. Mussaurus was a plant-eater that lived during the late Triassic Period, more than 200 million years ago. It is estimated that a full-grown adult would have been about three metres long.

The skeletons of the just-hatched Mussaurus babies are preserved in amazing detail. Their teeth are hardly as big as rice grains and their toe bones are not much larger.

Bonaparte's Carnotaurus skeleton was amazingly complete, lacking only parts of the feet and tail. It helped to put Argentina on the fossil-hunting map.

Argentinian palaeontologist José Bonaparte is one of the world's foremost dinosaur hunters. In 1985, he announced the discovery of a new carnivore that brought South American fossil hunting into the limelight.

Towering bull

Bonaparte's find was almost eight metres long and in life would have weighed more than a tonne. It walked and ran on its large back legs, with tiny, almost useless arms. It also had a small 'horn' above each eye, rather like a bull. So it was named Carnotaurus, meaning 'carnivorous (flesh-eating) bull'.

Colossal cousin

In the same year as the discovery of the giant 'bull', Bonaparte and his colleague Fernando Novas, from the Museum of Natural History in Buenos Aires, named another huge new meat-eater. This was Abelisaurus, a relation of Carnotaurus. It lacked head horns and lived near the end of the Cretaceous Period, whereas Carnotaurus came from mid-Cretaceous times. Abelisaurus grew up to nine metres in length and had a longer head and jaws than the flatter-snouted Carnotaurus.

Huge herbivores

In 1969, Bonaparte had described Riojasaurus, one of the earliest really large plant-eaters from almost 220 million years ago. In 1991, with his colleague Leonardo Salgado, he announced another long-necked herbivore – Amargasaurus. This beast weighed over five tonnes, and had a double row of spines along its neck and back. Perhaps in life these spines held up a long flap or double-flap of skin.

A pack of Aucasaurus (meat-eating relations of Carnotaurus) attack a Cretaceous titanosaur hatchery near Auca Mahuevo in Patagonia, Argentina.

Biggest so far

South America in the 1990s

THE 1990s WERE RECORD-BREAKING YEARS in South America. Several extraordinary finds beat long-held records, including some of the earliest dinosaurs known from fossils, the biggest meat-eating dinosaur and the most enormous dinosaur of all.

One of the first

In 1988, one of the great dinosaur hunters of modern times began to search in the Andes foothills of Argentina. Paul Sereno (see pages 72–73) was interested in the remains of a new meat-eating dinosaur found by a local farmer, Victorino Herrera, near San Juan. Sereno and his team recovered several more skeletons, one with a skull. The dinosaur was named Herrerasaurus, in honour of its original discoverer.

Earliest ever

Herrerasaurus was about three metres long with powerful back legs, small arms, and long jaws with small, sharp, curved teeth. It lived near the start of the Triassic Period, some 225 million years ago. In 1991, Sereno's team found even older fossils, dating back 228 million years. They were from a smaller meat-eater, only one metre long from nose to tail. This is one of the earliest dinosaurs so far discovered. In 1993 it was named Eoraptor, 'dawn thief' (see page 8).

Prospector Gabe Lyon sits among the late Cretaceous fossils of a huge, plant-eating titanosaur. To her left is an upper limb bone. This excavation was part of the 1990s treasure trove of dinosaur remains found in southern Argentina. Titanosaurs were the last of the sauropods and lived mainly on southern continents.

Discovering giants

In 1993, the largest dinosaur known so far was announced in Argentina. It was named Argentinosaurus by Rodolfo Coria, from the Carmen Funes Museum in Neuquén, and José Bonaparte (see pages 56–57). The fossils, found in Plaza Huincul, are not as complete as those of other famous giants, such as Brachiosaurus. But their shape and size are enough to show that the plant-eating Argentinosaurus was more than 30 metres long and 70 tonnes in weight – the largest animal ever to walk on Earth.

Most massive predator

In 1995, Coria and Leonardo Salgado named the largest flesh-eating land creature ever – Giganotosaurus. The record for the biggest carnivore was previously held for 90 years by Tyrannosaurus. The two looked quite alike, but Giganotosaurus was slightly larger – 13–14 metres long and seven or eight tonnes in weight.

Spare-time find

The first bone of Giganotosaurus was noticed in 1994 by car mechanic Ruben Carolini. He found the fossil while scouring the windy, rocky 'Valley of the Dinosaurs' in the south-east of Argentina's Neuquén province. The skeleton turned out to be two-thirds complete and was excavated by Coria's team from the Carmen Funes Museum. Its full name is Giganotosaurus carolinii, in honour of its original finder.

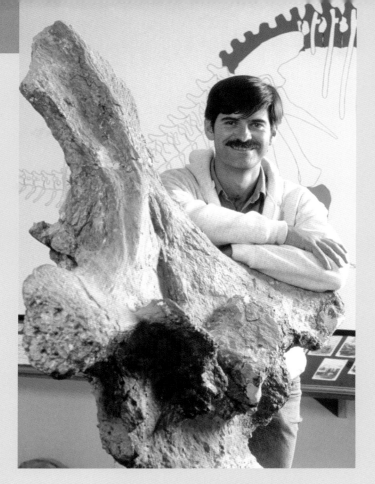

Rodolfo Coria poses with a vertebra (part of the backbone) of Argentinosaurus. Other fossils found belonging to this giant herbivore include ribs, parts of the hip bone, and a rear limb bone.

Coria dusts down a jaw bone of Giganotosaurus, the biggest known predator, from 100 million years ago. The valley where it was found was declared a National Monument of Argentina in 1997.

Activity in the Antipodes

Australia until the 1980s

Minmi remains (above) were found in a wide expanse of flat grass and scrub, where fossils are rare. They were named by Ralph Molnar (right).

ACROSS MUCH OF AUSTRALIA, THE ROCKS ARE either the wrong kind or the wrong age for dinosaur fossils. However, there are places where sedimentary rock from the Mesozoic Era does exist, and these have been the sites of some important fossil finds.

Downs giant

The first dinosaur fossil to be identified in Australia was found in the southern state of Victoria in 1903 (see page 62). However, many other early finds took place in Queensland, north-eastern Australia. Rhoetosaurus was discovered at Durham Downs, near Roma, in 1924. It was named in 1925 by Heber Longman (1880–1954), director of the Queensland Museum, after a giant from Ancient Greek mythology. Rhoetosaurus lived in the Jurassic Period, 170 million years ago, and was one of the early long-necked plant-eaters, or sauropods.

Small but armoured

In 1964, Ian Ievers and Alan Bartholomai found fossils of an armoured dinosaur, or ankylosaur – the first ever to be discovered in the Southern Hemisphere. In 1980, Ralph Molnar, who was then senior curator at the Queensland Museum, named this plant-eater Minmi after its discovery location of Minmi Crossing, near Roma, Queensland. Two partial skeletons of Minmi were discovered. They were attached to very hard rock, and acid chemicals were used to free the fossils. Minmi lived about 115 million years ago. It was very small compared to other ankylosaurs – about the size of a large pig.

Bulging beak

A third dinosaur from Queensland is Muttaburrasaurus, first discovered at Muttaburra by rancher Doug Langdon in 1963. Since then, further remains have been unearthed in various places, including the world-famous Lightning Ridge fossil site in northern New South Wales. Muttaburrasaurus was named by Ralph Molnar and Alan Bartholomai in 1981. It was a large plant-eater with a beak-like mouth, from the dinosaur group called ornithopods. Measuring about seven metres from nose to tail and weighing around three tonnes, it was a close cousin of Iguanodon. Muttaburrasaurus had a strange bulge or lump on its snout, in front of its eyes (see page 24).

Dinosaur stampede

In 1971, the story of a 'dinosaur stampede' unfolded at a site called Lark Quarry in central Queensland. A set of fossilised trackways, unearthed in the 1960s, were initially thought to belong to birds. But when palaeontologists investigated, they discovered that the prints were actually left by at least 150 small dinosaurs.

Also evident were the tracks of one huge meat-eater. It seems that the predator had pursued the herd in a frantic chase.

The tracks at Lark Quarry show at least two types of smaller dinosaur – some carnivores and some slightly larger herbivores. They all ran on two legs, as did the single meat-eating giant that chased them. This huge predator left behind distinctive three-toed footprints.

Dinosaur Cove

Australia from the 1980s

IN 1903, GEOLOGIST WILLIAM FERGUSON FOUND Australia's first dinosaur fossil. The site was a stretch of cliffs and bays on the south coast of Victoria state, close to Inverloch. In the 1970s the area was revisited by surveyors, and in 1980 a new fossil site was discovered nearby.

Difficult and dangerous

The new site, west of Cape Otway near Melbourne, seemed to hold the promise of many fossils from dinosaurs and other creatures. But the area was a difficult place to work. The cliffs and loose rocks were very hard, and sometimes they had to be blown apart with explosives. There were overhangs above and huge waves crashing below. Workers had to climb down the cliff on ropes or approach by boat and clamber up the slippery slope. Finally, in 1984, an expedition was organised from the Museum of Victoria, led by curator Thomas Rich.

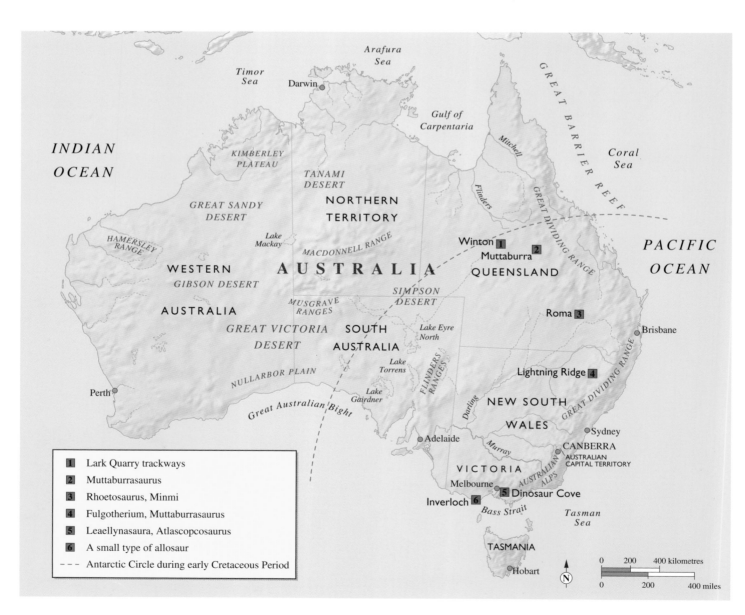

1. Lark Quarry trackways
2. Muttaburrasaurus
3. Rhoetosaurus, Minmi
4. Fulgotherium, Muttaburrasaurus
5. Leaellynasaura, Atlascopcosaurus
6. A small type of allosaur
- - - Antarctic Circle during early Cretaceous Period

Patricia Vickers-Rich and Tom Rich are fossil experts who work at Monash University, Victoria, Australia.

This warning sign of kangaroos on the road near Dinosaur Cove has been altered to show a stegosaur-type dinosaur. Unfortunately the warning is about 100 million years too late (and it is the wrong kind of dinosaur, too!).

Rich collection

Ten years of excavations followed at Cape Otway, revealing a marvellous selection of fossils. The site became known as 'Dinosaur Cove'. One of the major discoveries there was Leaellynasaura, a small, slender plant-eater only two metres long. It was named after a young girl – Leaellyn Rich, daughter of the expedition leader. Remains of several of these dinosaurs were dug out, including a well-preserved skull which revealed a beak-like mouth and huge eyes.

Leaellynasaura stood about half a metre tall at the hip and weighed around ten kilograms.

Coping with cold

The rocks at Dinosaur Cove date from the early Cretaceous Period, about 110 to 100 million years ago. At the time, the land-mass of Australia was so far south it was inside the Antarctic Circle. So the climate would have been cold, even frozen and snowy, during the long, dark winters. How did the dinosaurs survive the cold? Other fossils from the site revealed trees and various plants. Perhaps the small dinosaurs huddled together under a pile of vegetation and slept through the winter. The finds at Dinosaur Cove have raised many new questions about how dinosaurs lived and how they coped with extreme conditions.

Company name

In addition to Leaellynasaura, another small plant-eater found at Dinosaur Cove was named Atlascopcosaurus in 1989. This strange name is taken from Atlas Copco, a mining company that lent digging and excavation equipment to the fossil hunters. Another find was a 'dwarf allosaur' – a meat-eater similar to the huge Allosaurus of North America, but smaller.

Days of darkness

Dusk fell early during the long winters in mid-Cretaceous southern Australia, but Leaellynasaura's big eyes were suited to the gloom. At the sight of a predatory allosaur, one Leaellynasaura would shriek warnings to the others as they fed on soft water plants.

Isolated on islands

The West Pacific from 1975

ISLAND COUNTRIES SUCH AS JAPAN AND NEW Zealand have a history of being alternately above and below sea level. Their rocks have been twisted, distorted, heated and cracked by volcanoes and earthquakes. Hence few fossils have survived intact; most have been shattered, and finds in the West Pacific region are rare.

Tail bone in a stream

For many years, fossil experts assumed they would never find dinosaur remains in New Zealand. There were some fossils of ancient sea creatures but few from land animals. Then, in 1975, amateur fossil hunter Joan Wiffen found a tail bone in Mangahouanga Stream. She was not sure what kind of creature it belonged to. But in 1979–80, Australian museum curator Ralph Molnar (see page 60) identified it as part of a meat-eating theropod, broadly similar to Tyrannosaurus but much smaller. This was the first evidence of dinosaurs in New Zealand.

New Zealand mix

Since 1980, remains of several more types of dinosaur have been found in New Zealand. They include an armoured plant-eater, similar to Ankylosaurus but smaller, and a huge sauropod – possibly a type of Diplodocus – with a neck that stretched ten metres high. There are also traces of a plant-eating ornithopod, similar to Iguanodon but smaller, as well as fossils of many other prehistoric creatures including flying pterosaurs and various sea reptiles.

Luck in Japan

Among Japan's scarce dinosaur fossil evidence is a tooth found in the Fukuoka region in 1990. It was named 'Wakinosaurus' in 1992, although the specimen is too limited for a full official name. The tooth probably came from a large meat-eater, about ten metres long, which lived

The fossilised tail bone, or caudal vertebra, found in Mangahouanga was probably from a medium-sized theropod – a meat-eater that walked on its two back legs. The 'spike' pointing to the top left is the neural spine. It projected vertically upright from the backbone and was one attachment point for the muscles that raised the tail and swung it from left to right.

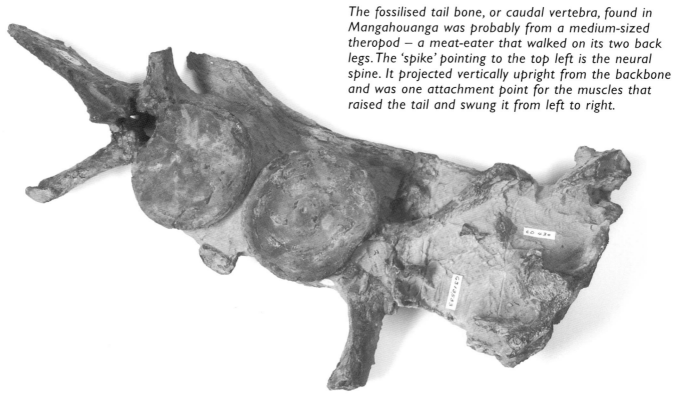

during the Cretaceous Period. Also, in the village of Nakasato in the Gunma region of Japan there are footprints that may have been made by an Iguanodon-type plant-eater. They have been closely studied by Yoshikazu Hasegawa, director of the Gunma Museum of Natural History.

Tricky tail

A third find, also in the Nakasato area, is a tail bone, possibly from a tall, slim ostrich-dinosaur. This has been called 'Sanchusaurus' although it may well be from an already-named species such as Gallimimus. There are fine displays of dinosaurs and other prehistoric creatures at the Kitakyushu Museum of Natural History and Human History, in south-west Japan.

Right: The Nakasato footprints show the trackway of an ornithopod — a plant-eating, Iguanodon-like dinosaur. The originally flat ground where they formed has been tilted at right angles, so the prints are now on a vertical rock face.

Below: This model 'Sanchusaurus' at Dinosaur Kingdom in Nakasato is reconstructed mainly on the evidence of one tail bone from the early Cretaceous Period. Future finds and studies may reveal that this dinosaur did not exist.

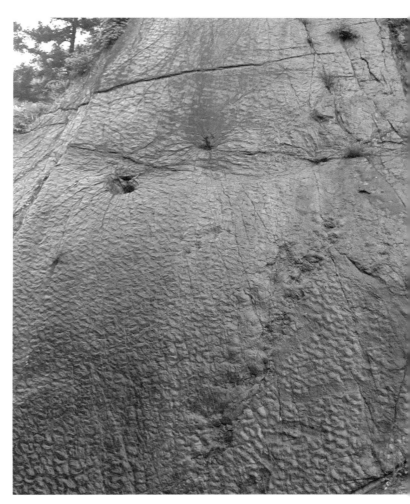

Dinosaurs near the poles

Antarctica and Alaska since the 1980s

TODAY, FEW LIVING THINGS SURVIVE IN THE polar regions. Places such as Alaska and Antarctica are covered with ice and snow, and endure bitter cold during their long, dark winters. But during the time of the dinosaurs, the climate was very different – this was partly due to the positions of the continents.

Finds in the far south

Dinosaur fossils had been found on every continent except the great southern land-mass of Antarctica – until 1986. Then, remains of an armoured ankylosaur were uncovered in the region of James Ross Island. Many more dinosaur fossils have been found on Antarctica recently, including parts of a small, slim plant-eater similar to Hypsilophodon (see page 81), a small meat-eater and a larger one, and a huge sauropod some nine metres in length.

Mass migration?

In Alaska, north-west North America, various dinosaur fossils have been discovered among the rocky, icy slopes. They include specimens of Edmontosaurus, which is one of the largest known hadrosaurs, at 13 metres long and four tonnes in weight. Its fossils have been found across a vast region of North America, from Alaska southwards to the centre of the continent. This suggests that these dinosaurs went on regular long journeys, or migrations, just as mammals such as caribou do today. Herds of Edmontosaurus would trek across the landscape, following food supplies of freshly-growing plants as the seasons changed.

Fossilised dinosaur skin is a rare find. Several specimens of Edmontosaurus skin have been uncovered. They show a thick and leathery texture, with scattered larger bumps surrounded by many small scales typical of reptiles.

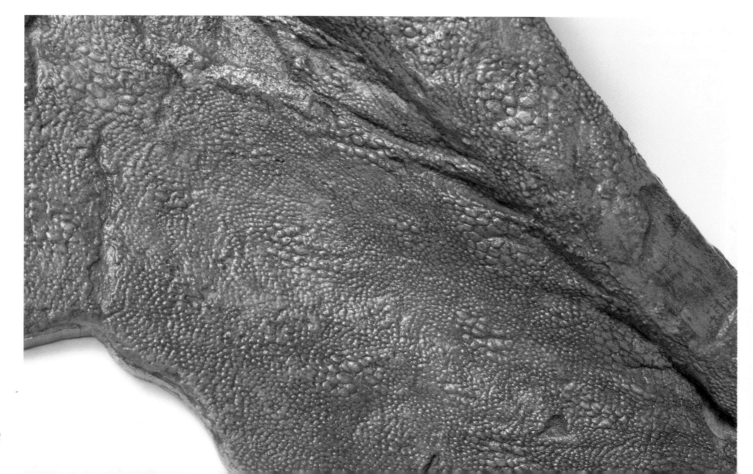

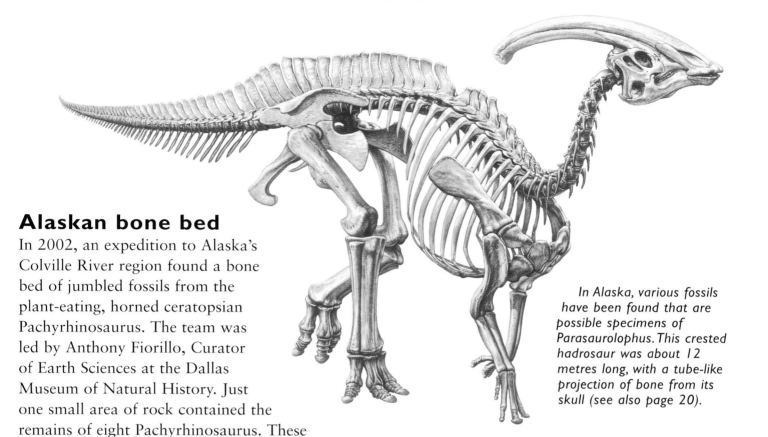

Alaskan bone bed

In 2002, an expedition to Alaska's Colville River region found a bone bed of jumbled fossils from the plant-eating, horned ceratopsian Pachyrhinosaurus. The team was led by Anthony Fiorillo, Curator of Earth Sciences at the Dallas Museum of Natural History. Just one small area of rock contained the remains of eight Pachyrhinosaurus. These bulky-bodied dinosaurs were about as big as elephants, with huge, horn-edged frills of bone around their necks (see pages 70–71).

Pachycephalosaurus males rammed heads as part of their breeding behaviour, trying to out-butt each other to win partners for mating. The tops of their skulls were greatly thickened with bone, acting like crash-helmets to withstand impact.

In Alaska, various fossils have been found that are possible specimens of Parasaurolophus. This crested hadrosaur was about 12 metres long, with a tube-like projection of bone from its skull (see also page 20).

More from the northern ice

The check-list of Alaskan dinosaurs continues to grow. It includes a type of ankylosaur, the large meat-eater Albertosaurus, the 'bone-head' Pachycephalosaurus, the three-metre-long plant-eater Thescelosaurus, and the small, agile, big-brained meat-eater Troodon.

Alaskan migration

During the late Cretaceous Period, vast herds of Pachyrhinosaurus (cousins of Triceratops) would follow a seasonal migration route to what is now snow-covered northern Alaska. Fellow plant-eaters, duck-billed Edmontosaurus, also made the journey to fresh feeding grounds for the brief summer.

Saharan treasures

North Africa from the 1990s

URING THE 1990S, SEVERAL REMARKABLE sets of fossils were found in the parched lands of North Africa. Much of the work was led by Paul Sereno, who had previously been involved in record-breaking discoveries in South America (see page 58).

African hunter

The first major find was Afrovenator – 'African hunter'. Its almost complete fossilised skeleton was unearthed in 1993 in Niger's Sahara region. Afrovenator was up to nine metres long and resembled other large predators like Allosaurus and Tyrannosaurus. It lived during the early Cretaceous Period, about 130 million years ago.

Jaws like a shark

In 1996 came news of an even bigger predator – a 14-metre-long cousin of Giganotosaurus. This was Carcharodontosaurus – 'shark tooth reptile' – a mid-Cretaceous dinosaur from 95 million years ago. Carcharodontosaurus was not a new name. It had been given in 1931 to fossils also found in the Sahara region. These specimens had been destroyed in the Second World War, but the new finds fitted their descriptions closely, so Carcharodontosaurus 'came back to life'.

In honour of Jobar

In 1997, Sereno's team excavated the almost complete remains of a huge adult sauropod in the Sahara Desert near Agadez, central Niger. The dinosaur was named Jobaria, after the mythical creature Jobar that features in legends of the region. There were remains of several individuals at the site, including a youngster. It seems that a herd could have perished together. Jobaria measured more than 20 metres from nose to tail and weighed an estimated 20 tonnes.

In the North African desert, Paul Sereno (left) and fellow excavator work to uncover the rear leg of the great long-necked plant-eater Jobaria. Between them is the thigh bone, or femur. The lower leg bones – tibia and fibula – are in front, with the ankle and toes in the foreground.

Crocodile rocks

In 1997, Paul Sereno and his colleagues found the fossils of a huge predator they named Suchomimus – 'crocodile mimic'. Its remains, from the Tenere region of Niger, suggested it was about 11 metres long and weighed perhaps two tonnes. The head and jaws were unusually low and long, with cone-shaped, slightly back-curved teeth, similar to those of a crocodile. Suchomimus may have been a fish-eater – when it lived, about 100 million years ago, the region that is now desert was scattered with pools and swamps.

Spiny family

Suchomimus showed many similarities to a dinosaur called Spinosaurus, fossils of which had been found in Egypt in 1912. Spinosaurus had long rods of bone sticking up from its back, which may have held up a sail-like flap of skin. Its remains were lost in the Second World War, but pictures and descriptions survived. The discovery of Suchomimus has helped to form a group of dinosaurs called the spinosaurs, which also includes Baryonyx (see page 80).

'SuperCroc'

In 2000, another Sereno expedition to the Tenere desert area unearthed a new giant – this time not a dinosaur, but an enormous crocodile. Sarcosuchus, or 'flesh crocodile', was twice as long as the largest living crocodile and more than five times as

Paul Sereno scrapes carefully at a fossilised claw of the massive theropod Suchomimus.

heavy. It lived about 110 million years ago and probably preyed on young dinosaurs, including Jobaria.

Paul Sereno with a life-sized model of 'SuperCroc' Sarcosuchus.

Carers and killers

North America from the 1960s

THROUGHOUT THE 20TH CENTURY, NORTH America continued to produce wonderful fossil finds. These did not break records as the biggest, fastest or first dinosaurs. But they have greatly influenced people's ideas about the way dinosaurs lived and behaved.

Clever claws

For more than a century, dinosaurs were viewed as slow, stupid, lumbering beasts. But a new find in 1964 changed these ideas. Fossils of several individuals were discovered in the 'Badlands' of South Dakota, by John Ostrom of the Peabody Museum at Yale University. They were named in 1969 as Deinonychus – 'terrible claw'. These raptor-type dinosaurs were about as tall and heavy as human adults and lived in Cretaceous times, some 110 million years ago.

Maiasaura was a nine-metre-long plant-eater from the hadrosaur group. It lived in the late Cretaceous Period about 77 million years ago. Maiasaura nests were found in close-knit clusters, scooped out of the earth.

Ostrom's studies showed that Deinonychus was anything but slow and stupid. It was reconstructed as an active, agile, fast and clever predator. Several sets of fossils together suggested that these animals may have hunted in packs, rather like wolves do today.

Mother instincts

In 1978, local historian Marion Brandvold and her son David came upon some small fossil bones near Bozeman, Montana. These were identified by John 'Jack' Horner of Princeton University, and excavations began in the area. The dig revealed many bowl-like nests, with fossils of eggs and baby dinosaurs among broken eggshells, preserved twigs, berries and plants.

Some of the babies' limbs were not developed enough for walking, yet their tiny teeth showed wear marks, as if they had been eating plants. This suggested that the parent dinosaur brought food to the babies in their nest, rather than just leaving them to fend for themselves. The dinosaur was named Maiasaura – 'good mother reptile'.

The story of 'Sue'

In 1990, experienced fossil hunter and explorer Susan Hendrickson chanced upon some dinosaur remains on private land near Faith, South Dakota. She was working for a team of professional fossil hunters and dealers led by Peter Larson of the Black Hills Institute of Geological Research. The remains turned out

to be from the largest and best-preserved Tyrannosaurus ever found. It was nicknamed 'Sue', after its discoverer, and became the subject of a legal battle about who actually owned the fossils. Finally 'Sue' was auctioned in 1997 in New York for US$7.6 million. She is now on display at the Field Museum, Chicago.

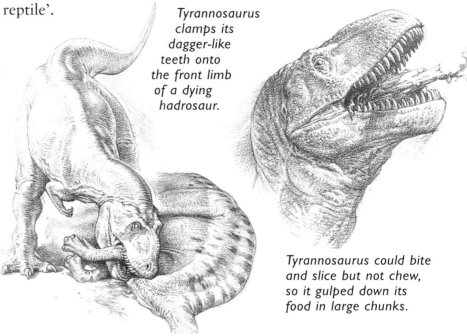

Tyrannosaurus clamps its dagger-like teeth onto the front limb of a dying hadrosaur.

Tyrannosaurus could bite and slice but not chew, so it gulped down its food in large chunks.

American fossil expert David Varricchio and his team work to shift the plaster-encased bones of Daspletosaurus, a smaller cousin of Tyrannosaurus.

Dinosaurs with feathers

Asia from the 1990s

IN THE LIVING WORLD TODAY, ANY CREATURE with feathers is regarded as a bird. But the prehistoric world was very different. Many experts believe that some dinosaurs had feathers, as shown by amazing recent fossil finds, mainly in China and Mongolia.

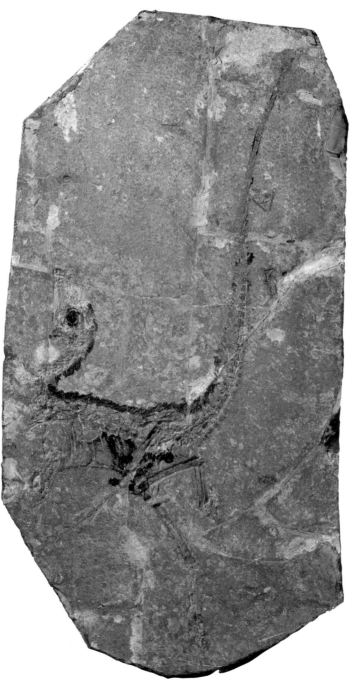

Bird mimic

In 1981, Russian palaeontologist Sergei Kurzanov described the fossils of a small, lightly built dinosaur and named it Avimimus – 'bird mimic'. The fossils came from the deserts of Mongolia and China and date back 85 million years. The front limbs of Avimimus were similar to bird wings in the way the bones were shaped and could move. There was also a strange ridge running along one bone of each arm, where in modern birds the flight feathers would be attached. So Kurzanov suggested that Avimimus had feathered arms, although these were not large enough or strong enough for proper flight.

A fluffy covering

In 1996, Chinese fossil experts Ji Shu-An and Ji Qiang announced another feathered dinosaur. This was Sinosauropteryx – 'China's winged reptile' – a lightweight meat-eater just one metre long. Its remains came from the Liaoning region north of Beijing, where the fossil-rich rocks are very fine-grained. This allows tiny features to be preserved, and traces of fluffy down feathers appear on the neck, shoulders, back and tail of Sinosauropteryx.

Four feathered limbs

Since the discovery of Sinosauropteryx, finds of feathered dinosaurs have been abundant, especially from Liaoning and other parts of China. One of the most extraordinary, in 2003, was a small carnivore only 77 centimetres long. This miniature meat-eater was given the full

Sinosauropteryx was a fairly standard small, meat-eating dinosaur, similar to Compsognathus (see page 84). But detailed study of its fossils has shown that it had many short, hair-like plumes or 'feathers', each five to ten millimetres in length.

name Microraptor gui. Its fossils showed long, stiff feathers on both the front and rear limbs, and a trailing, feathered tail.

Why have feathers?

Birds have different kinds of feathers. Long, stiff flight feathers push against the air for gliding and flying. Soft, fluffy down feathers help to keep in heat, since birds are warm-blooded and need insulation to maintain their body temperature. Perhaps dinosaurs had different types of feathers for the same reasons. Having down feathers, as on Sinosauropteryx, would mean that some dinosaurs, at least, were warm-blooded – not cold-blooded like today's reptiles. This is a subject of heated debate among fossil experts.

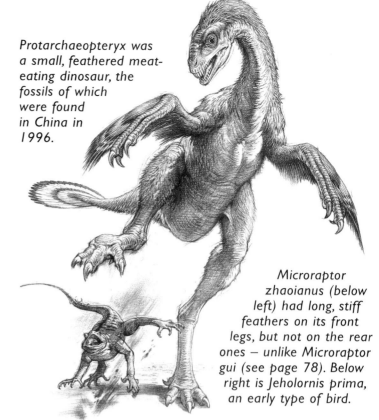

Protarchaeopteryx was a small, feathered meat-eating dinosaur, the fossils of which were found in China in 1996.

Microraptor zhaoianus (below left) had long, stiff feathers on its front legs, but not on the rear ones – unlike Microraptor gui (see page 78). Below right is Jeholornis prima, an early type of bird.

Microraptor

Microraptor gui is the only four-winged creature known to have lived. Its limb muscles were too weak for long flight, but it could probably glide skilfully for short distances, using its extended feathered tail for control.

Fortune in Britain

Southern England from the 1970s

THE ROCKS AND CLIFFS OF SOUTHERN England have long been famous for their fossils. Recent finds in the county of Surrey, and on the Isle of Wight off the south coast, have unearthed several new dinosaurs as well as various other prehistoric creatures.

Quarry claw

William Walker was a plumber and quarry worker in Surrey in the 1980s. His job gave excellent opportunities for his hobby of fossil hunting. In 1983, he came upon a huge, curved claw, as long as his forearm. Further excavation by experts from London's Natural History Museum revealed that it belonged to a ten-metre-long, two-tonne predatory dinosaur. It seems the claw grew on the first digit or thumb of each of the dinosaur's two 'hands'.

The full name given to this dinosaur (right) was Baryonyx walkeri, meaning 'heavy claw of Walker', after its discoverer (below).

Fishing for food

Baryonyx had an unusually long, low skull with narrow jaws and pointed teeth, similar in overall shape to a crocodile's head. Fossils of only one individual were found, but these included preserved fish scales in the stomach region of the skeleton, suggesting that Baryonyx ate fish.

Swampy surroundings

Other fossils showed that when Baryonyx lived, 120 million years ago, the area was a mixture of woodland, shrubs, pools and rivers. Perhaps this beast waded in shallow water and used its thumb claw to hook out fish up to one metre long.

Hosts of 'Hypsys'

Hypsilophodon was a slender, fast-moving plant-eater about the size of a large dog. Fossils of more than 20 'Hypsys' have been unearthed on the Isle of Wight. The first specimen, found in 1849, was studied by Gideon Mantell and Richard Owen and was initially identified as a young Iguanodon. But later discoveries showed that the teeth and many other parts of the skeleton were different. In 1869, the animal expert Thomas Huxley gave the dinosaur its own name, which means 'high-ridged tooth'.

Recent finds of Hypsilophodon show several individuals preserved together. Perhaps these small herbivores lived in herds, grazing on low plants and dashing away from danger like today's small deer and gazelles.

Hypsilophodon had a horny, beak-shaped mouth, with nibbling upper front teeth and plant-shearing rear teeth. Its hands had five fingers, which was a common feature of early or 'primitive' dinosaurs.

Dinosaur Isle

Wonderful fossil discoveries continue on the Isle of Wight. In 1978, remains of a large meat-eating dinosaur were noticed in cliffs along the south-west coast. In 1996, after further finds and studies, the new dinosaur was named Neovenator, meaning 'new hunter' (see page 82). The full name – given by Steve Hutt, then curator of the Isle of Wight Geological Museum, and his colleagues – is Neovenator salerii. It commemorates the Salero family, who owned the land where the fossils were found.

In 2001, the collections of the Isle of Wight Geological Museum were moved to create the Dinosaur Isle centre at Sandown. This houses not only local dinosaur finds including Neovenator, Hypsilophodon and a brachiosaur (see page 88), but also fossils of sea reptiles and flying pterosaurs. In fact, the Dinosaur Isle building itself is in the shape of a pterosaur.

Neovenator

Neovenator was a large predator, eight metres long and similar in shape and build to Allosaurus of North America. It lived in the early Cretaceous Period, about 120 million years ago.

Fresh finds in Europe

Germany and France from the 1970s

Two of mainland Europe's most famous prehistoric creatures – the tiny dinosaur Compsognathus and the first known bird Archaeopteryx – were discovered well over a hundred years ago. But there have also been exciting recent finds in Europe, especially in southern Germany and France.

The first known bird

Archaeopteryx, or 'ancient wing', was given its name in 1861. Its fossils have all been found in the Solnhofen region of Bavaria in southern Germany. They range from a single feather to an almost complete individual, set in fine-grained rocks that show many tiny details. The feathers' structure is similar to the flight feathers of birds today, suggesting that Archaeopteryx was not limited to clumsy gliding. However, the bones of its shoulders, chest and wings show that the flight muscles were not as big or as strong as in modern birds. So Archaeopteryx could probably flap and fly, but not very far.

Tiny carnivore

The meat-eating Compsognathus, 'elegant jaw', lived at about the same time as Archaeopteryx, in the late Jurassic Period. At 70 centimetres in total length, it is one of the smallest dinosaurs known from relatively complete remains. Its first fossils were found in the 1850s in southern Germany, but another, larger specimen emerged in 1972 in the Var region of south-east France.

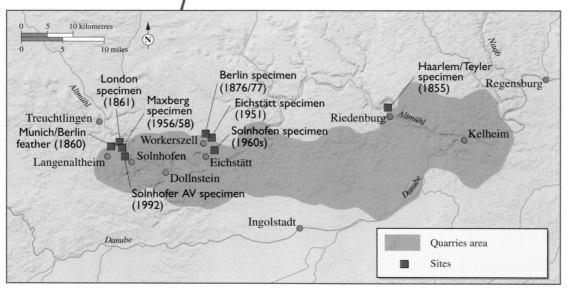

The Solnhofen limestone quarries cover more than 100 square kilometres of southern Germany. They have been home to all of the world's Archaeopteryx finds, from 1860 to the latest in 1992. The dates on the map show when the fossils were found.

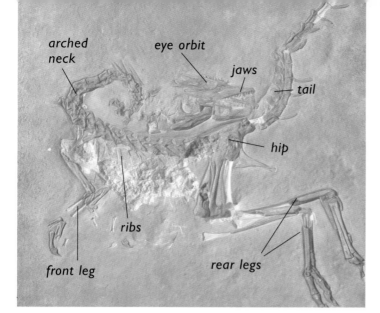

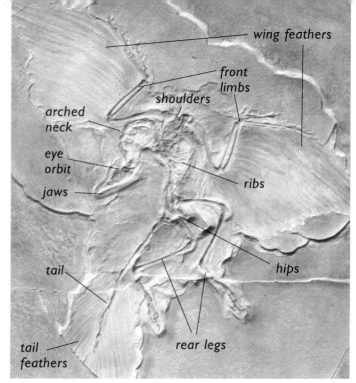

These fossil specimens of Compsognathus (above) and Archaeopteryx (right) have many similarities, not only in their general skeleton but also in the 'death pose', in which the head arches up and rearwards over the back.

Var region raptors

France's Var region was the site of another great find in the 1990s. Spare-time fossil hunters Patrick and Annie Mechin uncovered the partial skeleton of a meat-eating raptor, nearly two metres long. It included pieces of a skull, teeth, limb bones, and the large, curved claw that raptors have on the second toe of each foot. The find was named in 1998 as Variraptor mechinorum, after its location and discoverers.

Less complete fossils of a similar dinosaur from France were named in 2000. The remains were noticed after a forest fire, so they were given the name Pyroraptor, meaning 'fire thief'. Further finds and studies may show that

Variraptor and Pyroraptor were actually the same kind of dinosaur.

Dinosaur on the wall

In 2001, a new kind of early plant-eater was named Ruehleia, in honour of German fossil expert Hugo Ruehle von Lilienstern (1882–1946). The remains had originally been identified as Plateosaurus, a similar long-necked plant-eater known from many finds around Europe. Apparently the fossils were noticed in a display mounted on the wall of a German castle. Further studies showed that they were different enough from Plateosaurus to be given their own name.

Fossils of Archaeopteryx show some variation in size, from as small as a magpie to almost chicken-sized. The average beak-to-tail length is 60 centimetres, and weight estimates are around 300–400 grammes.

Dracula the dinosaur?

Eastern Europe and Western Asia in the 20ᵗʰ century

DINOSAUR DISCOVERIES ARE NOT ESPECIALLY common in Eastern Europe or Western Asia. But one fossil, found in 1925, caused headlines when it was first announced 50 years later. It was given the full name of Bradycneme draculae.

Creative name

Bradycneme means literally 'slow shin'. The fossil is part of the rear leg, from the lower shin and ankle region, including the ankle joint. It is similar to the same part of the body in the agile meat-eater Troodon. However, the Bradycneme specimen suggests a sturdier, slower-moving leg for this type of dinosaur. The second part of the name, draculae, comes from the region where the fossil was uncovered – near the Transylvanian home of the legendary blood-sucking villain Count Dracula.

Mistaken identity

The single Bradycneme fossil is flimsy evidence for naming a new dinosaur. In fact, before a dinosaur connection was realised, some experts said that the bone came from a huge prehistoric owl! Other scientists suggest that the remains of Bradycneme could be from the dinosaur already known as Elopteryx. This was named in 1913, on the basis of part of a thigh bone and other fossil fragments. However, the Elopteryx evidence is also somewhat insubstantial. Whether Elopteryx and Bradycneme were actually Troodon-type dinosaurs, and if so, whether they were both the same kind, is still open to question.

Action in Western Asia

In 1968, Russian fossil expert Anatoly Rozhdestvensky named a medium-sized herbivorous dinosaur from Kazakhstan. It was called Aralosaurus, after the huge lake known as the Aral Sea. But its remains, which include parts of the skull, some backbones and limb bones, have not been backed up by more recent discoveries.

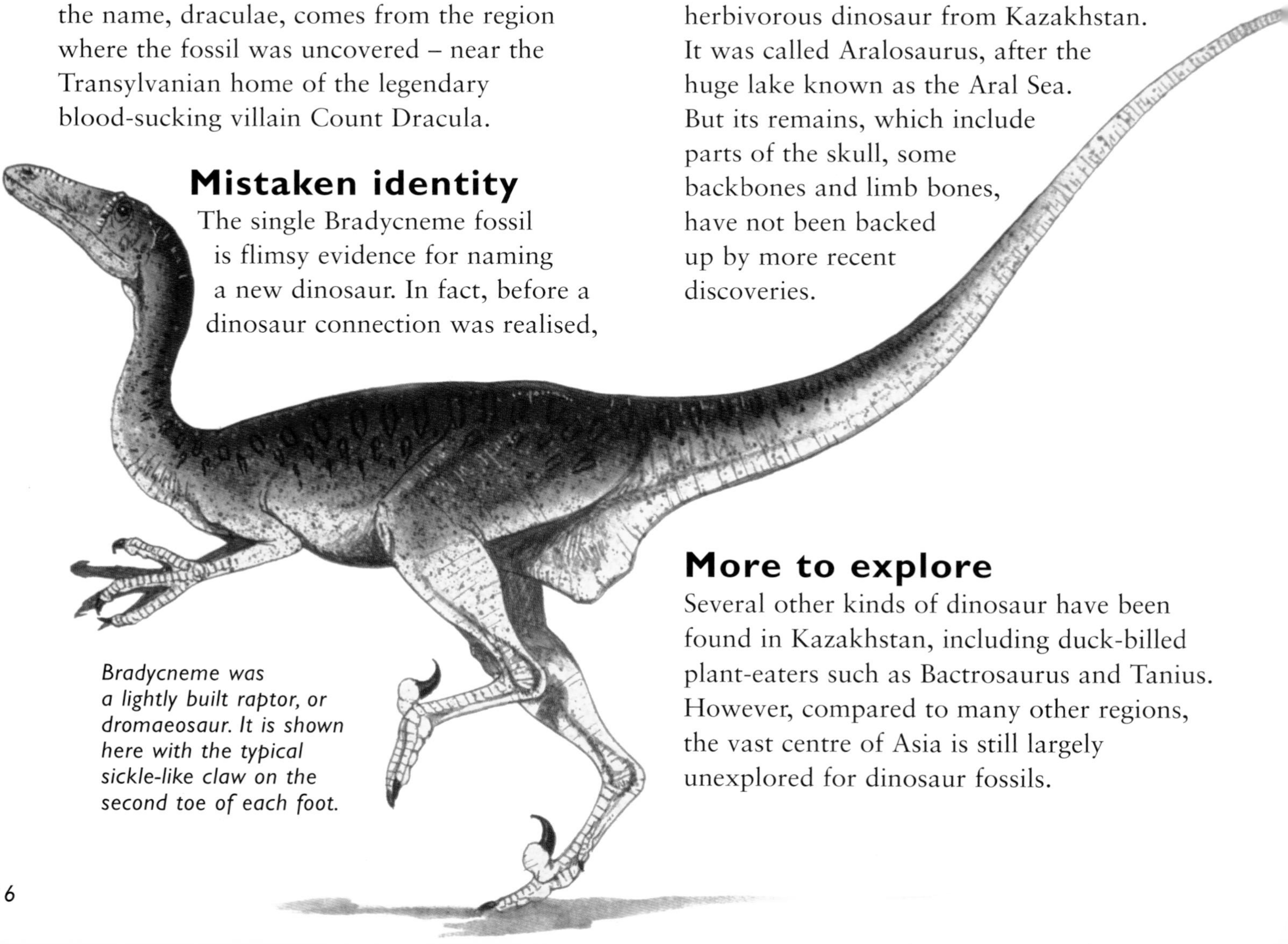

Bradycneme was a lightly built raptor, or dromaeosaur. It is shown here with the typical sickle-like claw on the second toe of each foot.

More to explore

Several other kinds of dinosaur have been found in Kazakhstan, including duck-billed plant-eaters such as Bactrosaurus and Tanius. However, compared to many other regions, the vast centre of Asia is still largely unexplored for dinosaur fossils.

A colourful character

Elopteryx has the full name of Elopteryx nopcsai, in memory of one of the most extraordinary dinosaur hunters – Baron Franz Nopcsa von Felso-Szilvas (1877–1933). Born into a rich Austro-Hungarian family, Nopcsa became interested in dinosaurs after fossils were found on land belonging to his sister. He went on to study and name many kinds.

Names galore

Nopcsa's finds included the smallish duck-billed plant-eater Telmatosaurus; a small, plant-eating species of Mochlodon (now listed as Rhabdodon); the armoured Onychosaurus (which Nopcsa 'un-named'

Baron Franz Nopcsa von Felso-Szilvas was a dinosaur hunter and part-time spy.

and withdrew from the list after just a few months); a species of Camptosaurus (now regarded as Rhabdodon); a species of the small, armoured herbivore Struthiosaurus; plus a tooth possibly belonging to a large meat-eater like Megalosaurus, which he called Megalosaurus hungaricus.

Never satisfied

In his hectic life Nopcsa was also a geologist, a biologist, a military commander, a spy, a motorcycle enthusiast and a speaker of several languages. He even tried to become leader of Albania! He finally died by shooting himself after doing the same to his companion.

The hadrosaur Telmatosaurus – 'marsh reptile' – was the first dinosaur Nopcsa named, in 1903.

European giants

Spain and England since the 1990s

EUROPE HAS MANY FOSSILS OF DINOSAURS, but few from true giants. Two recent discoveries of huge, long-necked sauropods, however, have changed this picture. One find was made in Spain, the other in the Isle of Wight off the south coast of England.

Island giant

In 1992, fossils of a huge sauropod were found on the south-west coast of the Isle of Wight. The initial discovery, by Gavin Leng, was a neck bone about 75 centimetres long. Later, another neck bone was found. The remains were uncovered by the wearing-away of seashore rocks that date back to the early Cretaceous Period. They represent a long-necked plant-eater similar to Brachiosaurus, over 20 metres long and weighing 40 tonnes or more. It is the largest dinosaur known from Britain.

The Isle of Wight once trembled under the footsteps of huge brachiosaurs, which could crane their necks as high as a modern four-storey building.

Delving at Riodeva

The remote and mountainous region of Aragon in Spain is scattered with orchards of almond trees. Local people had cleared these areas of 'stones' for centuries. But in 2003, palaeontologists Rafael Royo and Alberto Cobos discovered that the stones at a site near Riodeva were actually shattered dinosaur fossils.

Huge clues

An excavation team was called in. Led by Luis Alcala, director of the nearby Teruel Palaeontological Foundation, experts began to dig very carefully. Initial finds included a humerus – the bone in a dinosaur's upper front leg, equivalent to a human forearm. This single bone was 178 centimetres long – as tall as an adult person. Another find was a sauropod toe claw, a huge 40 centimetres in length.

Europe's largest dinosaur

Most of the Riodeva remains lay just under the surface. Further work uncovered parts of the pelvis (hip bone), ribs, and more bones from the limbs and toes. Scaling up the finds to make a whole sauropod gave the creature a nose-to-tail length measurement of more than 30 metres and a weight of perhaps 50 tonnes. This is the largest dinosaur known so far from Europe.

Spain in Cretaceous times

There are fossils of other dinosaurs, including stegosaurs, at the Riodeva site, as well as remains of crocodiles and fish. These suggest a lush landscape of rivers and lakes during the early Cretaceous Period. Based on publicity from the finds, a dinosaur theme park called Dinópolis was opened in the local town of Teruel. Apart from exciting rides and other attractions,

Luis Alcala shows science reporters part of the site at Riodeva, where fossils lie amid jumbled rocks and soil.

visitors can watch experts cleaning and restoring the fossils through the glass wall of the palaeontology workroom.

Young visitors meet Tyrannosaurus among displays at the Dinópolis museum. Remains of this meat-eater have not been uncovered at the nearby Riodeva site, but fossils of huge plant-eaters are plentiful.

Finds for the future

The world from now

THE QUEST FOR DINOSAURS IS FASCINATING, partly because it is full of surprises. Almost every year, fresh fossil finds come to light and new kinds of dinosaurs and other prehistoric creatures are announced.

Fossil family

Sometimes a find advances our knowledge of dinosaurs into new areas. In 2004, a stunning discovery from Liaoning, China showed the 'parrot-beaked' dinosaur Psittacosaurus – a plant-eater about the size of a large dog, that lived 125 million years ago. The remains included one adult with 34 youngsters grouped around it, all within a bowl-shaped area. The discovery was made by local farmers and has been studied jointly by Jinyuan Liu of the Dalian Natural History Museum in China, and David Varricchio of Montana State University, Bozeman, USA.

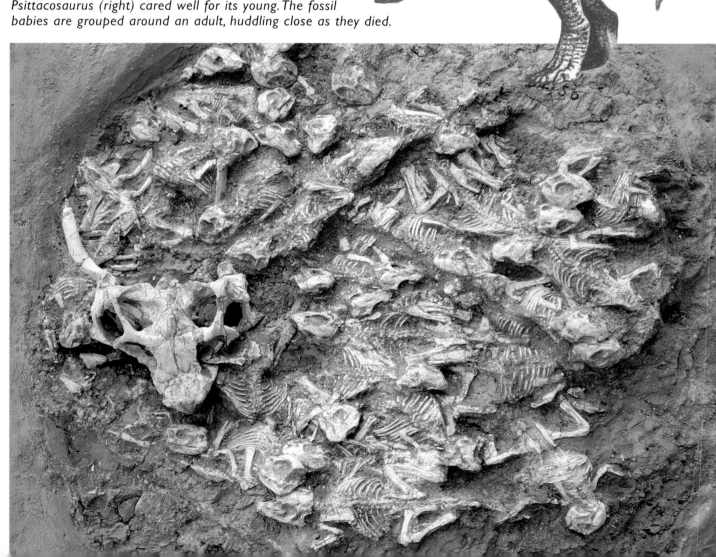

Psittacosaurus (right) cared well for its young. The fossil babies are grouped around an adult, huddling close as they died.

Dinosaur nursery

There seem to be too many Psittacosaurus young in this group to belong to one female. They are also part-grown, rather than newly hatched. The suggestion is that young from several mothers gathered in a nest under the continuing care of one adult, as a type of 'dinosaur nursery'. This behaviour is known today in birds such as the ostrich. The find indicates that dinosaurs not only looked after their own young – an idea that until recently was laughed at – but that they even cared for the babies of others.

Sudden death

The Psittacosaurus skeletons are amazingly complete. This suggests that there was no time or opportunity for their bodies to be picked and gnawed by scavengers. The whole group must have met its end very quickly, with the young clustered around the adult for protection. Perhaps they drowned in a flood, or choked to death from fumes poured out by a nearby volcano. They could well have been trapped when their nesting burrow collapsed. This extraordinary find has offered yet more intriguing clues about the life and nature of the dinosaurs.

Constant change

It is currently estimated that more than 1,000 kinds of dinosaur have been discovered. Some types are well established from many complete skeletons. Others are based on just one or two fossils, such as a tooth or a toe bone. The list of types changes continually as new finds affect old ideas. Doubtful names are regularly struck from the list, while new possibles are added.

Living for ever

The list of fossil hunters who are remembered for important finds is constantly extending, too. Professional palaeontologists often achieve lasting recognition as new kinds of dinosaur are named after them. Part-time and amateur fossil sleuths are also occasionally honoured. Sometimes they stumble across finds on their first expedition, by chance or by accident. But usually their discoveries are the result of endless hours spent scanning the ground, digging away soil and chipping at rocks, in hopeful pursuit of a marvellous new specimen. The dinosaur quest is tough, but it continues to thrill the world.

Sometimes old methods are still the best – in this photo from 2001, mules are being used to haul protected fossils across 'Badlands' terrain in Montana, USA.

Glossary

Allosaurs A group of large, meat-eating dinosaurs with tiny front limbs that walked on two back legs. The group includes Allosaurus, which lived mainly in North America during the late Jurassic Period.

Ankylosaurs A group of plant-eating 'armoured' dinosaurs, protected by thick lumps and shields of bone in their tough skin – for example Hylaeosaurus.

Asteroid A huge lump of rock, smaller than a planet but larger than a meteorite, moving around the Sun. Some asteroids have lopsided paths or orbits and may collide with each other or with a planet.

Bone bed A huge collection of bones and other preserved items, usually lying jumbled together in an area that has 'more fossils than rocks'.

Bone-head Also known as a pachycephalosaur. A plant-eating dinosaur that moved mainly on its rear legs and had a greatly thickened upper skull, like a crash helmet – for example Pachycephalosaurus.

Carnivore An animal that eats mainly other animals, usually their flesh.

Ceratopsians A group of plant-eating 'horned' dinosaurs with rhino-like horns on the nose and/or eyebrows, and a wide ruff or frill of bone around the neck – for example Pachyrhinosaurus or Triceratops.

Cold-blooded An animal that cannot make heat inside its own body, and so depends on warmth from its surroundings or environment to raise its temperature enough to move about and stay active.

Cretaceous Period The third period of the Mesozoic Era, lasting from 135 to 65 million years ago.

Cynodonts A group of meat-eating, mammal-like reptiles (therapsids), probably warm-blooded and with fur or hair, that lived during the Triassic and early Jurassic Periods. Most were cat- or dog-sized.

Dicynodonts A group of plant-eating, mammal-like reptiles (therapsids), with hooked, beak-like mouths, that lived during the Triassic Period and before. Most were pig-to-cow-sized.

Dinosaurs 'Terrible reptiles' – reptiles that shared certain bodily features and lived during the Mesozoic Era, becoming extinct at its end 65 million years ago.

Dromaeosaurs A group of meat-eating, usually smallish dinosaurs with long, pointed teeth, powerful, sharp-clawed fingers and strong rear legs with a large 'sickle claw' on the second toe of each foot.

Evolution The gradual change in living things through time, as new kinds or species develop and existing ones die out or become extinct.

Extinct When a kind or species of living thing has died out completely. When many species disappear around the same time, this is called a mass extinction.

Femur The bone in the upper part of the rear limb, equivalent in a dinosaur to our own thigh bone.

Fossils Remains of once-living things, both plants and animals, usually preserved in rocks and turned to stone over millions of years.

Gondwana The southern group of major land-masses formed when the super-continent Pangaea began to split during the Jurassic Period.

Hadrosaurs A group of fairly large, plant-eating 'duck-billed' dinosaurs with wide, flat, beak-like mouths, long, powerful tails and larger back legs than front legs – for example Edmontosaurus.

Herbivore An animal that eats mainly plant foods, from leaves and flowers to roots and shoots.

Humerus The bone in the upper part of the front limb or arm, equivalent in a dinosaur to our own upper-arm bone.

Ichthyosaur A fast-swimming, predatory sea reptile with fish-like fins and tail, resembling a dolphin in overall body shape.

Jurassic Period The second of the three time spans in the Mesozoic Era, lasting from 203 to 135 million years ago.

Laurasia The northern group of major land-masses formed when the super-continent Pangaea began to split during the Jurassic Period.

Mesozoic Era Time of 'Middle Life' – one of the major time spans (eras) of Earth's history, lasting from 250 to 65 million years ago.

Migration A long journey undertaken by animals, usually at a regular time or season each year – for example between a summer breeding region and a winter sheltering area.

Ornithopods 'Bird-feet' – a large group of plant-eating dinosaurs that walked mainly on their two bigger back legs. Ornithopods included small types, such as Hypsilophodon, and larger ones such as Iguanodon and the duck-bills, or hadrosaurs.

Ostrich-dinosaur A tall, slim dinosaur with a beak-like mouth, a long neck, smaller front limbs and very long, strong but slim rear limbs for running fast. Also known as an ornithomimosaur. Gallimimus is the best-known example.

Palaeontologist An expert on fossils and the rocks containing them.

Pangaea The super-continent formed when all Earth's major land-masses came together as one during the Triassic and early Jurassic Periods.

Pelvis The hip bone, joined to the backbone (vertebral column) and the upper bone, or femur, of each rear limb.

Pinacosaurs A sub-group of the plant-eating ankylosaurs, including the five-metre-long, late-Cretaceous Pinacosaurus, which lived in Eastern Asia.

Plesiosaur A sea-dwelling reptile with a long neck, wide body, short tail and four flipper-shaped limbs.

Prosauropods A group of medium-large, plant-eating dinosaurs, with small heads, long necks and tails and wide bodies, that walked on all fours – for example Plateosaurus or Riojasaurus. Prosauropods, or 'before sauropods', were generally smaller than their later relations, the massive sauropods.

Pterosaurs Flying, reptile-like creatures, mostly with long-toothed beaks and furry bodies, that lived during the Mesozoic Era. They are sometimes called 'pterodactyls', although Pterodactylus was only one of many kinds of pterosaur.

Raptor 'Thief' or 'plunderer' – a name often used for the dromaeosaur dinosaurs – for example Velociraptor – as well as for other hunting animals such as eagles, hawks and other birds of prey.

Sauropods A group of generally huge, plant-eating dinosaurs with small heads, long necks and tails, barrel-shaped bodies and four column-like legs – for example Brachiosaurus or Diplodocus.

Sedimentary rock Rock formed by sediments such as sand, silt, mud or clay, which usually settle in layers on the bottom of a sea, lake or river, and are squeezed solid by more layers piling up on top.

Spinosaurs A group of large, meat-eating dinosaurs that moved mainly on their rear legs, each with a long, low, crocodile-like skull and jaws – for example Baryonyx or Suchomimus.

Stegosaur A plant-eating, 'plated' dinosaur with a small, low head, a humped body, four strong legs, and spikes or plates of bone sticking up from its back – for example Stegosaurus or Tuojiangosaurus.

Therizinosaurs A group of plant-eating, 'scythe-claw' dinosaurs with longish necks, bulky bodies, strong rear legs, and very long claws on their front feet or 'hands' – for example Therizinosaurus.

Theropods Meat-eating dinosaurs with sharp teeth and smallish front limbs, which walked and ran mainly on their larger rear legs. Theropods ranged in size from tiny Compsognathus and Microraptor to huge Allosaurus, Giganotosaurus and Tyrannosaurus.

Titanosaurs A sub-group of the huge, long-necked, plant-eating sauropods. Titanosaurs included Argentinosaurus and Saltasaurus, which lived mainly during the Cretaceous Period in the southern continents of South America and Africa.

Trace fossils Signs or items left by creatures such as dinosaurs, including footprints, scratch marks or coprolites (preserved droppings), rather than parts of the animals themselves.

Trackway A series of preserved footprints or paw marks of dinosaurs or other creatures.

Triassic Period The first of the three time spans in the Mesozoic Era, lasting from 250 to 203 million years ago.

Vertebrae The row of bones which make up the spinal column or backbone (vertebral column) of creatures such as dinosaurs and other reptiles, birds, mammals and fish.

Warm-blooded An animal that can make heat inside its own body and so is able to keep its temperature high enough to move about and stay active, even when the surrounding conditions are cold.

Index

Entries in **bold** relate to pages with illustrations, maps or photographs.